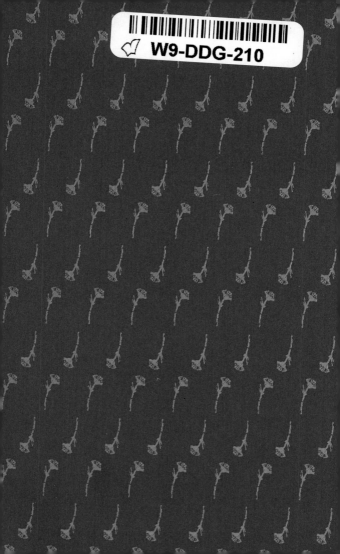
W9-DDG-210

EUROPA ERLESEN | EDITED BY LOJZE WIESER

Ein Projekt von Graz 2003 Kulturhauptstadt Europas
www.graz03.at

EUROPA ERLESEN
GRAZ

Edited
by
Markus Jaroschka and Gerhard Dienes
in collaboration with
Alfred Kolleritsch, Herbert Piwonka
and Karin Jaroschka

About Antonia's

Hometown

from her

Vater.

Wieser *Verlag*

Wieser Verlag
A-9020 Klagenfurt/Celovec, Ebentaler Straße 34b
Tel.: +43(0)46337036 Fax: +43(0)46337635
office@wieser-verlag.com
www.wieser-verlag.com

•

Wieser Verlag expresses its sincere thanks to the holders
of the rights for their kind permission of publishing.

Titels of texts were partly chosen by the editors.

Unless otherwise specified all texts
translated by Tim Sharp.

Copyright © of this edition 2003 by Wieser Verlag,
Klagenfurt/Celovec
Copyright © of various texts see list of references
All rights reserved.
ISBN 3 85129 394 0

Ante scriptum

Everyone talks about Europe. We don't. We read it. We'd like to take you along with us. There are over sixty volumes to date in german language. Although we have apparently come closer to our original goal of portraying a Europe from Iceland to Greece, from Portugal to the Baltic and the Carpathians, nevertheless while on the road the signposts and orientation aids have led us ever deeper into unplumbed depths of literature.

Doesn't the topography of literature lead us to places we've encountered in that literature over the centuries but which aren't (and won't be) associated in people's consciousness with a concrete location?

Literary currents appear at first glance to leave no recognizable traces behind but just as underground rivers don't vanish simply because they are no longer visible, those currents are are, however, formative influences even when initially manifested as spatial taboos of reception. To give the world narrative form must also mean to imagine a literary map which is cognisant of space in literature.

The literary gaze is perhaps in a position to draw the fine-grained structure of a region and also to transform mountains, rivers, roads people (and their thoughts, feelings and memories) into captivating narratives. Perhaps it is also able and, indeed, most suited to the task of bearing these impulses out of the place themselves into new places, to plant them in new geographies but leave their naturalness and originality.

As long as we only see how literature rescinds spatial laws but not how deep-rooted it is nor its point of origin then Fernand Braudel will wait for a long time for an echo. In his three volume contribution to the cultural history of the Mediterranean he wrote »that we have museums catalogues at our disposal but not art atlases; art and literary history but no cultural narratives«. We would only add that we feel the absence of cultural narratives and literary atlases as a lack. So we decided make our own cartographic contribution to a European literary atlas. Read up on (and across and deep into) Europe. Make your choice.

Whether in the series EUROPA ERLESEN or in the works of individual authors, whether in the present or far back in the past, it is literature which casts a spell.

And isn't it something nice to be spellbound?

That's why we want to take you on our travels. This time in English. Try Graz, Ljubljana and Vienna.

Contents

H. C. ARTMANN

(1921–2001)

graz

graz:
you tend no zoo
go your own way
macaws are foreign to you
your okapis, chamois
all around nature laughs
hilly land good hats
always in front of your eyes a
happy piece you
take care of the viola
you bequeath: overcoats
alpine Pleiades
lohengrin the grace of
pleasure garden and opera
you people it oft
you are never alone
the auk likes you
the sun plus moon
the zebras of love
whether the mur oh
your young lady plays
how can you prove it?

FRIEDERIKE MAYRÖCKER

(∗ 1924)

In the Winters

… the starry skies over Graz in the months of October and November as if I would walk into a hail of bullets. The Great Bear with lop-sided fringed forehead staggering in its crystal runners (a horde of children). The names begin to evaporate from my memory except perhaps Cassiopeia or the Swan and I set out in one direction with a destination I'll never be able to reach

which is to say I have already started out. Towards Ortweinplatz. Until my hands congeal to lumps of snow and my feet too, it was snowing. I went over Quay Bridge, I am coming from Griesgasse, I step out of the hotel. I moved in here for a few days months years, or into the greening palm tree courtyard, the grove of the Archduke Johann where the hotel guests swim around like the deep-sea fish do until their time has come. I remember it I spent a long time looking at a glass dome that simulated the depths of the sea.

Pince-nez of the lens – all around the lovely falling-snow sky crystallises I am in a fever of impatience, cloudy wisdom thunders deafeningly in my ear. From the snowed-in backyards come hollow-sounding harmonicas and musical clocks. I count the chimes. From the market side precisely panting pretend laughter, echoing. I avoid the threatening stare of a steel skeleton on the other side of the street, something is being built here, my heart pounds. I plumb the depths of my intentions, its can't be so very far to go. She will be waiting for me colourful pinafore circumspect-tender preparations, something steamy stewing. In the live-in kitchen souvenirs of the newly dead in black frames.

Restrained behaviour till my hands and feet go numb, a cold-catching condition, probably. Someone calls over from the nearby flea market – I'm the frame king!

I had no other choice, I had to fly at the insect with a heavy terry towel. It came buzzing up from the flower petals, bounced off my forehead as I was putting the flowers in water to keep them fresh for the visit, it wasn't loud but I heard it like a trombone, suddenly the ethereal waves had washed something up and it sloshed around so much in the cupboard, a revolving sound whose acoustic focus appeared to distort in ever more attractive ways communicating captivating feelings of well-being and protective constancy.

She still saw the child in me! The baby, the new born, the happy expectancy of my parents! In the bathroom you could still see right into my depths, so innocent and unclouded. The first house after the bridge to the left I had to ask a number of times. She had probably never read Péguy, I always loved her. The baby carriage was tilted backwards so I lay with my head downwards, between window and window, the wind blew cold over my brown downy skull.

Until the hands and feet numbed, feeding the birds above the Mur. I had a slight fever, the doctor pretended to sympathise, in the bathroom, the hot towels the bags of ice. Perhaps she had broken, tread on, a mirror beforehand, – oracular prophesy.

The doctordoctor in the round wing of the institution surrounded by bear-like figures I observe the windscreen wiper long how it industriously fans against the pelting rain (defend against everything, smear, hide, dry out, blood clot, tears) until I take the trouble, myself as the rubber floor tiles on the right, pushed back to the centre of the window as soon as the most furthest away angle is reached. Damp-counter resistance in the depths of my intestines, how many hours to Graz by car?

lop-sided, fringed forehead, jay, bird desire Péguy, and waiting in order to be able to wink at him a little without the others immediately noticing, he leans on the doorpost and stares at nothing. From a bear-like figure as if in fur clothes, a huge black bear, mounted, in the sky. I jumped on him from the back just as he wanted to cross the yard of the Krebsenkeller pub to get back to the smoky barroom according to

previous experience I would have quietly folded my hands over his eyes from behind, and teasingly asked him who is it? could he guess? and tilted backwards into the fallen snow so we were both locked together, in the swirl of the snow turned around backwards, each of us, each after a few steps looking for our own footprints and whether they are quickly blown away.

Until my hands and my feet grew numb. To feed the birds above the Mur. Above the Mur walking by way of Gries Quay, on your knees, rosary mill milling nibbling, crater landscape of the morning toast, rivulets, dried up, table seated, it rustles casually newspaper-leafy. In the morning again the slightly white-wise flags, cirrus over the stretched-out blue, later sweeping with feathers. What in the world did he want to read from the stars last night?

I suddenly feel smaller than him and only reach up to his shoulder. I nestle into his downiness, a will-less dedication an exchange of souls – doctor and patient – I read these days about it. Comb, fetish, of an eagle, chief giant (cock's plumage). The head of my doctor. My psychic dependence, cirrus, white plume. I cower in his self-tensioning wing formed in silver. In feather dress at the first impulse, spitting fire with a gaze of heated promise.

It has a southern touch he said, almost like Padua.

Down there the Mur. Fantasy veduten.* The car drives venereally in his arms in the bathrooms clumps of snow. Restrained behaviour, until the feet, the hands numb till I get into a cold-catching condition, probably. I was also a little delirious. With difficulty I swayed, the doctor simulated sympathy.

Concretising something that's only present as a rough idea he said to me on the telephone. It falls, you'll like it, I stopped his flow of words. I loved it when he unfolded the world for me. There was a pause in our conversation as perfect as if each of us had

---

* From the Latin, a landscape painting done to scale.

pressed a shell to our ears to catch the roar. That with him I ever, went through my head, was a real wonder it had been a confusing tension between he and I right from the beginning.

I went a little further in the same direction I must be very close to the junction of the two streets from where you can see into Ortsweinplatz. I was late she'll be waiting for me but she wouldn't be impatient she'd be hoping that I was coming.

I stopped in front of a news kiosk and read the bold-face letters without understanding them then I went a few steps further towards the place I had struggled to get to

but I knew I had already moved away from it long ago.

INGE MORATH

(1923–2002)

I simply feel at home here ...

At first glance the city doesn't appear to me
to be very mysterious but you can do
something with
everything.

ALFRED KOLLERITSCH

(* 1931)

Reciprocated love

What happiness and what life there could be in this city! There are but few who do not see its attractions. Graz has something about it you see at first glance, a little of the south inhabits the sultriness, one talks of the beautiful women (and overlooks, perhaps, that the alleged great numbers come from the fact that there are only a few of the streets are full of people). In the evening and on holidays the city dies, sad Sundays destroy the idyll. The city's breathing slows then. On days like this the city rejects itself. The foreigner asks in vain for the life he wants to become part of. Graz is a weekday city afraid of fantasy. The young reproduce the fashions, individual attempted breakouts don't last long (not even with the bad cuisine). They are more likely to try and get rid of each other, than to make allies of each other in mutual respect and against the overwhelmingly superior force. The biggest evil, however, preventing the counterweight of a new city being formed, is the stewing in your own juice, local rivalries, lack of experience. Thus superior powers of indifference blot up the opponents in this confined space because they get in each others way or get on each others nerves. Their contentious fights are deadly for those well-disposed towards art. The boredom of their opponents is also deadly, their interminable sameness, their strategy of driving the more lively to hopelessness and surrender so that some of the sons and daughters of the city become silent about Graz. They don't even want the reciprocated love offered them any more because they don't need a connection to the city anymore. They live the paradox that outside the province they are associated with Graz, the Graz being talked about a few years ago, above all at a time when this new Graz had the old Graz presented to it as a moral example.

ERICH FRIED

(1921–1988)

The Stairways of Graz

for A. Holzinger

For four hundred and eighty years
stone upon stone
the stones they bear:
A double spiral flight of stairs
grey Gothic
and posing questions.

In the tower
to the left of the arched gate
I look in
and questions pile up
like one stone on another:

Who invented this double spiral
stairway?
Was it made for a fairy tale
or for a dream?
Since you climb
both stairs at the same time
and at every step
you meet yourself and stay silent
find yourself in the other
and fall out
This double spiral binds
and twists space
with time ...

With time gone by
which never leaves you in Graz:
The Turk on the house –
and on the plague picture
Turk and plague.
And the stairs in the town hall
surrounded on all sides: Upset
you stand on the gallery,
free to the courtyard and quite open.

And the other stairs,
on the cliff face, seen from Castle Square
there I can climb zigzag
up to the clock tower
and look down
on the towers and roofs and lanes:
When I'm in Graz
I can't stop climbing stairs

to look again
at portraits
of long-dead women and men
till surfeited with the living age.
Because even when a lane is named
after the New World
it is still the old world spirit
that holds me fast
gently enveloping.

H. C. ARTMANN

(1921–2000)

news from north and south

… and once i went up the züriberg by tram along with
wolfi bauer to visit old joyce and it was already just
before six when the cemeteries shut and we didn't
find the grave anymore and had to go over the wall to
get free because in the meantime the cemetery had
shut and wolfi bauer drank only a quarter litre that
evening he was tired and i drank three litres and was
not yet tired but i hadn't driven the long way from graz
to zurich in one go all the way through gentlemen that
is a long way even for a lonesome cowboy but in
predigergasse susanne has her self-made arum schnapps
standing in the smallest witches' kitchen in the world
and i said where am i and tina said in evil hands that's
what the anti-fairy story demands but it was a special

time of trash and valium and everyone was pleased with us and waved bunches of flowers or gentian posies and the police tried not to rub people up the wrong way and the rockers politely doffed their toupees when we appeared in fantasio but i want to break off this litany just as i broke my heart when i went to nürnberg from negligence and afterwards landed at lückl's in graz with a psyche made of medical cotton wool and bubble gum and a time began out of kalmus* and valium and i was still alive although i had been kindly pronounced dead seven times good day mrs haring hello mr haring jesus it's mister artmann i didn't recognise you with the sunglasses mr bisinger was here again just a short time ago but is gone again to berlin with two litres of kalmus yes to be a student in graz when the lavender blooms all this is a sweet tangy shock without end a theme for hand, foot and mouth painters an alligator sticks his greedy maw out of the persil foam flood of the mur predatory piranhas stalk the southbound sailing sloop of the night boatman from mariahilferplatz a rampaging elephant bull roars macaws and cockatoos in city park drenched in gaslight on jakominiplatz a herd of antelopes and gazelles a blue gorilla which appears out of münzengrabenstrasse a boa constrictor in front of the safari group fleeing from a brown bear in the kälbernen quarter mucki nekrepp as a refuge for desert wanderers half dead from lack of water who have now reached the jungle the moon appears shining like the lamp of

---

* alcoholic drink

a lad-in need over the ruckerlberg main square kurt takes the safety off his henry carbine a lonely poet sings calming songs for female termites at kodolitch's stanley meets livingstone and kolleritsch records the short conversation on tape thanks you freddy that went down in history i carry my typewriter in a knapsack through city the heavy thing presses painfully into my back oh i wish i had never travelled to these green parts of the world stayed at home with my father and mother with my loving relatives if a scornful country cousin saw me he would be beside himself with malicious pleasure in front of the one-time ring cinema my fate rushes towards me as if he had grown up out of the earth young poet klaus stands in front of me swinging a bottle of paddy whisky i awake at any moment on a park bench and look at my watch it is always three in the morning i notice that i am slopping around in the bermuda triangle as helpless as a wasp in oil now at last i know what it means when you say he well oiled or not oiled that is the oil hill[*] and that is the crux of drinking companion life but let's forget that today is sunday after a long wait a halfway decent weather rosa has opened as is her want all the windows in the house and the semi-hot wind blows the rose petals from the wilting stalks onto the ground that looks nice i will insist that they don't sweep them away please leave it it looks nice burgis in friaul makes wonderful dolls and collects rose petals by the pound in tubs or is it stone basins the scent

---

[*] Ölberg lit. Oil Hill viz. Mount of Olives.

is weak but pretty individual a fire beetle that runs across the window sill dreams of rose petals in walburgis palladio villa in his fire beetle ears sounds a dwarfishly shrunk a breeze of past and coming earthquakes he lifts his feelers and stops he has six legs and two wings he steps forward lifts off and flies through the window into the open air his vermilion helmet shines in a sunbeam that comes from the thick branches of the aspen it is the tree in which my daughter always sees the witch the devil take me why don't i see any witches in the trees anymore in the last few years one of my faculties seems to have got lost am i supposed to have become adult and reasonable is it about time i passed on my business to upwardly-striving griseldis forced by circumstances to bequeath her my fantasy retiring to my little room and the wind rustles ...

FELIX MENDELSSOHN BARTHOLDY

(1809–1847)

Yawn

It is a boring place made to yawn in ...

WOLFGANG BAUER

(* 1941)

Graz

Windless jungle
on the plain a frozen tortoise
your life laboriously
protected by cooking
your electric orange-lit heart
in which artificial young ladies ask each other:
What prospects do I have?
or young boys say:
I live right out on the edge of the city.
Your blurry sky trembles
above the lukewarm streets
that peep carefully round the corner.
Strange arsehole of the world
that never shits!
Left and right lidless glass goggle eyes
gaze fixed on the beyond
and have to look upon everything there.
The hell-hounds lick chemical foam from the Mur
tremulous poets
spill red wine on their wine-red modern velvet.
In the city park it's dark.
The quiet tramway at the end of a winter night
might be your stroke of fortune.

FRIEDRICH NIETZSCHE

(1844–1900)

A Funny Figure

I had Miss Resa von Schirnhofer visiting me for a few days before she leaves, bound for her parents in Graz; she is a funny creature who makes me laugh and gets used to me rather well. This winter she will continue her philosophical studies in Paris.

The good Resi Schirnhofer was also there with one of her female friends from Zurich. It's a pity she, to use the vernacular, looks so ›ungraceful.‹ I can't stand ugliness near to me for very long (I meant that, in relation to Miss Salomé, I would have to overcome certain things in myself).

HANS LEIFHELM

(1891–1947)

The essence

Returning after a longer period of absence I feel the summer magic of the city as something special. The streets encumbered by a white midday sun, the deep stillness of a June day hanging over the garden, the breath of a lime-tree, chestnut or plane, the luminous play of colours amongst roses and gladioli, the rushing mountain water in the river bed; all of this unites to give the picture of a settlement filled with the essence of alpine countryside but which also hints at the traits of a southern landscape ...

RUDOLF STIBILL

(1924–1995)

Graz – A Myth

Graz is my Prague, my Dublin, my illness,
that hasn't stopped even after twenty years
in my region that a boy might bridge
with a stone's throw from the North Sea Canal
to the Eider – a stagnating and reed ringed
water that wends its way to the North Sea
against its will through wide and greening plains.
And Graz is – childhood and youth – a myth,
the future of what a city is:
the interplay of many people in many cafés.

ROBERT MUSIL

(1880–1942)

I am prevented from becoming
a writer in Austria

I am denied the possibility of being a writer in Austria.

My father spent the whole of his childhood and youth in Graz, attended school there – from infant's school through to taking his engineer's examination. He felt himself a Grazer his whole life and it was extremely hurtful for him never to have been offered a post in the ›Technical‹ there. It was pure coincidence that he was born in Temeswar and died in Brünn, an involuntary citizen of the Czech state.

His father moved to Graz in his mature years. He chose to live in it and was a doctor there. He became a farmer on a piece of land he settled down on, near to the city. But he had been born in Rychtarow in Moravia.

His (My great-) grandparents on his mother's side lived and died in Salzburg. My grandmother (father's mother) was born there. My grandmother on my mother's side is buried in Salzburg so the cemetery there has three of my forbearers.

My mother was born in Linz.

Her father was one of the four men who built the Linz-Budweis railway and was later in charge of it and I, myself, remember the grand villa in a wonderful garden that was the house where my mother was born and spent her childhood. Thus this grandfather, a not insignificant part of the local history of Linz, was born in Bohemia.

I myself was born in Klagenfurt.

I spent my childhood in Steyr and the accent there is the deepest Upper Austrian you could ever wish for.

Even Rosegger is a relative of mine though marriage.

But none of the provinces values me or claims me as their own ...

Nevertheless, I am naively convinced that the writer has a responsibility for humanity and apart from that I want to be a great writer. Which is an amour propre I hide well from myself.

DŽEVAD KARAHASAN

(∗ 1953)

The Identity of the City

Graz is one of those cities that makes me ask a number of questions about myself and that's one of the reasons I always want to come back here. There are a great number of questions, but here I want to concern myself with the question of the »Identity of the City.« So, what is Graz? A city in Central Europe? Of course. An Austrian city? Without doubt. You can see that at first glance. But there are places which make it perfectly plain that Italian architects did extensive work here and have had a decided influence on the face and atmosphere of the city. Thanks to these architects a facet was added to its identity, a little AND so that Graz became a Mediterranean city. And on top of that ...

But let's leave that, because those are not the kinds of question that made Graz so attractive to me. Practically any city worth its salt has this sort of amalgam of urban diversity, assuming, that is, that it has the appropriate age, size and wealth. Without this mixture it's not a city. The city of Graz however, poses questions of a quite different class. They are so unique, so characteristic for Graz that you have to talk about them as if they were very intimate affairs. One of these questions came to my attention during my first visit to Graz in 1988 when I made my very first appearance at a public reading in Forum Stadtpark. Since then I have been lastingly impressed by the love those in the city show Stadtpark. At the time I was just as irritated by the low opinion expressed in the relationship of the city to its squares. The attention lavished on the parks as well as the rejection of the squares is so striking that it immediately comes to the attention of a visitor on his first walk in the city. So our visitor starts to ask himself a multitude of questions about the appearance of the city and its flair. That grips the poor fellow so much that, filled with enthusiasm, he decides to ascertain the truth by asking experts, inhabitants and lovers (and I know many people in Graz who are in love). And since that time he comes back again and again, just as often as the opportunity presents itself. (...)

I don't have to tell you, dear reader, of the beauty of the Stadtpark and the other green spaces of the city. Or about the devotion with which these gardens are individually laid out, tended and cared for. However, the roots of the disregard as far as the squares are concerned would certainly interest me. The area in front of the blue grammar school (when you come out of Herrengasse and go through Hans Sachs Gasse) is predestined to be a square and might, indeed, have been the wonderful square every Mediterranean city would have been proud of. In order to prevent exactly that, the Raiffeisen Bank building was erected and the word square doesn't appear in any of the names around there. What of Jakominiplatz which has been turned into a traffic junction? Or Hauptplatz which they have stuffed full of kiosks, market stands or little sausage stands? The large monument in the middle of the square is literally overgrown with young people snacking on the steps around the plinth and the town hall also loses much of that »bureaucratic strictness« centres of municipal power usually give off because of the market activity on the square in front of it. Do you know of any other city with a main square like this?

Just so that we understand each other properly, dear reader, I have to confess to you that I really do have a soft spot for squares but that Graz's ignorance on this point is still not something that bothers me. Quite the opposite, it affords me pleasure that even the main square has nothing pathetic about it but is something so clearly there for the use of the people and not the city authorities (by leaving the city hall free standing with a huge un-built space in front of it). It lies in the ›nature of this city‹ that the cathedral and the town hall have not been built on the same square as is normally the case. It is probably for this reason that the scant regard given to squares is so strongly felt in this city. Basically it means it bothers no-one that squares worthy of a city simply don't exist. Should one (such as Jakominiplatz or Hauptplatz) have come into being despite all that, a way has always been found to somehow camouflage it.

Is this disregard really so deeply rooted in the nature of the city that no-one notices anymore? What is it's relationship to the enthusiasm for parks? Would the city lose some of its identity if squares were accorded more attention? Would I still love Graz as much as I do? Question after question, as with every true love where the lover bases their identity on these AND grounds, on uniqueness, individuality and not on belonging.

MARKUS JAROSCHKA

(∗ 1942)

home [heimat]

from the yellow woods
the autumn woods
the birds came back

into the city
that knew my breath
in which i lived
silently with the day
lived again and again
the closed dream in a cleft night

i didn't answer
the dusty houses
the concrete gazes of the gaping windows
i didn't answer
long didn't answer in shrieking poems
the ferocity of the real pictures

stone years

compounded
sensible of the panic-stricken silence
in soft, old earth words …
but out of the autumn woods
the birds came
summer birds
that no-one knew any more
back to the city

(spring might be coming)

KENKA LEKOVICH

(* 1963)

That time in St. Petersburg
(or How Graz Straightened Me Out Again)

>*I must have lived at various times in this house because I remember immediately in the streets of Prague and in the harbour of Trieste, I dream in Bohemian, Windisch*, Bosnian I was always at home in this house ...«*

(I. Bachmann, Malina, W. 3,99)

It couldn't have begun any better. No better than with an invitation to a spiritualist session which my well-disposed host knew nothing about, by the way. How could he have, occupied by his work as he is, one hand on the telephone the other on the computer and if he had had a third one he would have wished for a fourth. A fatal idea to unite 1. a human being, 2. a philosopher, 3. a mathematician, 4. a publisher, 5. a writer and 6. a poet in the guise of a single person. Points 5. and 6. are in no way interchangeable. So, as my host calculated how many hands he lacked he made compromises he would later regret (he would have been happy with a part-time secretary). He answers the telephone, faxes, catalogues, publishes, sends mails and signs his signature. The small table

---

* A small Slavic ethnic group

where he allowed me to sit, a graceful, round piece from the Twenties, started to have an effect. Tap. The little table parries the first blow, tap, tap, another two or three raps, it rises, tilts dangerously to the right, finds its balance again but suddenly, indignantly, you could say, it tipped completely to the left and buried me under thirty kilos of transLOCAL Project from, at a rough estimation, 15 issues of the respected literature magazine from the years 1996–2000.

I could have imagined all of this in my head coming from a romanziera di frontiera[*] except being buried alive under a city avalanche in Graz. So here I lie under Krakow, Pécs, Temeswar, Lemberg, Sarajevo, Brno, Trieste … Trieste, that meschugge[**] city where I come from after I had already come from and even meschuggier meschugginess than … At this point I'm allowed to make a comment about my so-called home city if it's true that we have to remember where we came from first of all in order to understand where we going to. This city, which is known as Fiume-Rijeka-St. Wiet on the Pflaum-Flumen sancti Viti as well as other things is, in fact, the meschuggiest of all. I use the word meschugge on purpose because only the truly crazy are really free and never was a city freer (or crazier) than my so-called home city. For 45 years, the years of communist rule, the meschugge city had the temerity to represent the Capuchin flag as its own. That wasn't much use when the communist regime

---

[*] Border authoress

[**] meschugge, Yiddish = crazy

was swept aside by the nationalistic papists. Instead of hoisting the Sahovnica[*] like the rest of world I unpacked the old independence flag – beautiful in the three colours yellow-black-maroon and not another word about it. And indeed no more words were exchanged but canon shots were; directly aimed at it, my city and by those who came from our capital. They aimed directly at the theatre built by Fellner and Helmer and thus at all theatres built by those two in honour of their apostolic majesties. That's what they thought. But the canons were completely rusty and exploded in their hands.

So you can see for yourself that with the Translocal perspective everything takes on a new meaning. It is only now, from this Translocal perspective that I see my fellow native city dwellers with the eyes of the world and understand that the real native of Fiume and basically Anyone of Our Time[**] has little choice but to be cosmopolitan, a rootless individual par excellence, Ödön von Horváth reproduced ad infinitum. So here I lie, buried under Krakow, Pécs, Temeswar, Lemberg, Sarajevo, Brno … My only hope is that my host doesn't notice any of this. That's exactly how it is. It's not every day you're buried by Krakow, Pécs, Temeswar, Lemberg, Sarajevo, Brno …all at the same. Just one would be enough to make me happy, Lemberg, for example. Take Leopoldi. At any moment I could meet Joseph Roth in L'vov, right from the beginning I could develop a plan for a nice Joseph Roth biog-

---

[*] The Croatian flag
[**] A work by Ödön von Horváth.

raphy and present it to a particular Soma Morgenstern who, due only to coincidence, had been in Lemberg before me and permitted himself to snatch the opportunity of my life from under my nose. This time I'll be there first and you'll lick your lips at my Joseph Roth biography. It will be a masterful literary feast of a kind seldom seen.

Or Sarajevo. Due to the laws of quantum physics and chaos theory which state that the beat of a butterfly's wing in Peking today might cause the end of the world in New York a month hence, my presence in Sarajevo could deflect that fatal bullet to a less damaging target, it doesn't matter which one, just not the one we all know about. Or Brno, just think of all the things I could offer to sell you on Tändelmarkt, not even Johann Stiasny, doctor of the devilish arts, could imagine so much. Already I can see myself wandering at night from one border pub to another and there I am in Brno. In Brünn ... I negotiate here with ghosts as my host suddenly reminds me that I might be hungry. But no, no, what's he saying, I'm just about to answer, but not after everything I've devoured on the way to Brünn.

Luckily there's a knock on the door. My host cannot imagine the trip I've treated myself to in the 4 minutes he took to talk to the lector from St. Petersburg on the telephone. Oh, yes, St. Petersburg was missing too.

»What was that, excuse me, did you say something?«

»No, not really, no. I just wanted to say that I like your city, that the air in Graz is most agreeable. It mixes the atoms together, swirls them, exactly. People should be brought to Graz more often.«

My host puts on his beret, turns off the computer, waters the aspidistra and accompanies me out into the October air that smells of jabuke u šlafroku, baked apples. He can't know that at the moment we are already in St. Petersburg.

But are we sure that he can't?

HANS WEIGEL

(1928–1991)

An Encounter between Gamsbart[*]
and Headscarf

In the swarming markets of Rathausplatz, Kaiser Josef Platz and Jakominiplatz you can feel one last times, perhaps the only time ever, what used to belong to Austria – Marburg (today's Maribor), Agram (today's Zagreb) Laibach (today's Ljubljana), Hungary too, and Poland and Bukowina a final echo of the colourful, farming, Slavic-Hungarian-Ruthen-Adriatic-gypsy people conglomeration that once stretched

---

[*] A tuft of chamois hair, bound and used as a decoration on men's hats.

from the middle of Europe far to the east and regarded Vienna and Graz as being in the far west, a final encounter between gamsbart and headscarf.

REINHARD P. GRUBER

(∗ 1947)

Graz is splendid

Graz is splendid. In Graz everything is different.

There are beautiful, wide streets in Graz and all of them lead through the inner city of Graz. The streets are so wide that all the pedestrians have space and on top of that there is enough for trams and cars. You're dazed from all the space the city offers to everybody.

Probably many merry riders also ride through Graz, but I don't get up early enough because the horses prefer to ride into a dewy dawn. That's why I always imagine how the horses ride without really riding. Manes flutter in the wind of their movement and the riders as well.

Every time I'm in Graz, I'm happy to be in Graz and many other Grazers are too. My granny takes me by the hand and we get on and when we get off we're in Graz. We go to Kastner and Öhler* and I get an ice cream. I travel with the escalator from right at the

---

* A large department store

bottom up to the 1st floor, then we make a bend and go up to the 2nd floor, then we make a bend again and go up to the 3rd floor. There granny takes quick look and then we make a bend and go up to the 4th floor. On the 4th floor it's finished because escalators only ever go as far as the 4th floor. They don't go any higher than the 4th floor because, like my granny says, the air would be too thin up there. Escalators don't go up high mountains either! We go very low down then and my granny buys a chamber pot in the grocery department below. She has it wrapped up right away so that nobody can see it, but in Graz nobody looks at chamber pots anyway. That's what's great about Graz.

JOHANN GOTTFRIED SEUME

(1763–1810)

A Jovial Little People

The Grazer are a good, social, jovial people who generally speak a slightly better German than the Viennese. The nobles are said to have an ancient pride. That is its overall spirit, sometimes a little rougher, sometimes finer, with the possible exception perhaps of the larger cities and larger residences where people rub up against each other more and smooth out the differences. Along the Mürz and the Mur downstream there are some old castles on the left and right which are sinking into ruin more and more thank

God. The sight of them increases the romanticism. Iffland, who was here last year, is still spoken of with enthusiasm, as in Vienna.

GÜNTER WALDORF

(∗ 1924)

In the end I left the emigration to the others

I was born in Graz and have just stayed there, ibidem. After consideration, I left emigration to others. The friends I encouraged found happiness in Canada. I just picked up my suitcase and got out of the train again in Graz Central and didn't have far to go to get to Keplerstrasse.

Some people think that it's a good thing for the city that I stayed here, as artist and well-spring of ideas. That's a great honour for me.

Some wonder whether my case at the time was empty or stuffed full. Whether I gave in to my affection for my home city at the last moment or whether I had come to a considered conclusion days before to stay rather than go. I can't remember any more and even if I could, it would remain my secret.

BARBARA FRISCHMUTH

(* 1941)

Graz: Key City

The last time I was in Graz I got a room key at the hotel reception desk which had number on it not to be found on any room. I wandered around for a while – probably I had not paid attention to something I had been told – until I found a employee of the house who opened the door to the room reserved for me. It really did have another number, why, I don't know. Maybe two rooms had been put together or a door had been moved or something. I got used to it very quickly and was too shy to ask because I was sure that I had originally been told the story in reception and just hadn't taken it in.

When I think about Graz it's the same as if I would try to lock something with the wrong key. No city in which I've ever lived is so familiar and at the same time so foreign ...

When I go for a short walk, I catch myself trying to follow the inner and not the outer geography, to overlook its present form. That's how much the city has become a memory for me. The seven years I spent here weigh so much more heavily than all the other visits I have made put together that nothing from them really connects me to the city other than this one memory ...

I made contact with a group which was only considered to be one afterwards but one thing certainly led to another. Studio Styria. I wrote programmes about Turkish and Hungarian literature. They were repeated years later by Hessian Radio.

But it still remained a very isolated city. When I sat on the wide widow sill of my room at night and watched the sparks from the shunting locomotives, I was sometimes afraid I would be strangled by all the different rails – including the Graz – Köplack line – that surrounded the house where I lived in Steinfeld. And I remembered the Sundays when I was afraid of being overwhelmed by loneliness.

I can't say that I have loved this city nor that I hate it. A kind of emotional numbness comes over me when I ask that sort of thing. It was never my city. It is a beautiful city which I still like today, a place of remembrance not of longing. Perhaps I even fled this city, all those years ago, but I'm not sure. Maybe it simply let me go ...

URS WIDMER

(∗ 1938)

Almost like Home

The snow had melted, fog crept through the streets and the air consisted mostly of carbon monoxide. I had drunk a coffee in the »Erzherzog Johann« and eaten an entrecote steak with onions in the »Krebsenkeller«. It was the place where the city had once welcomed me with a slap in the face. But the landlady didn't remember me and I didn't remember her and she had such small hands and was so young that she could perhaps have been the daughter of that monster with the gigantic paws. With a bunch of bank employees figured a way I could convert a few of my university schillings into Swiss francs more or less honestly – I had signed many forms in many offices. It was supposed to make me something equivalent to a native civil servant, with social security and the right to a pension. Once I had climbed up Schlossberg and had looked down on the city, at the windows of the little flats in the enormous palace in which I had once lived for a few weeks in the Seventies and where a concierge had watched over me as in a fairytale age, making sure that I didn't bring any women back and harm them. In order to get to my floor, the third or sixth, high up in any case, I had to grope through the pitch black halls of an historical museum that was just being refurbished. Sometimes I stumbled over an iron virgin or chain mail glimmering in the moonlight and gave myself a terrible fright. In the meantime the museum was open and illuminated and the palace, full of hanging cobwebs at the time, was now freshly restored. It shone and glowed. The car wreck in the courtyard had disappeared. I felt almost at home and considered staying amongst all this freshly renovated beauty but what would I to do if I didn't have any money. No little niches anymore, like there had been before. No box-rooms for half a franc a month as there once were. Still, some things were the same. A beautiful city. Where I arrived for my third hour at the

university – still a lot of people; I began to believe in
their loyalty – I already felt completely comfortable.
I put on my spectacles – I only saw my audience in-
distinctly now, like fish in an aquarium – and said ...

FRIEDERICKE SCHWAB

(* 1941)

My City

only from abroad
did my city
call to me of its terror

drove air shafts
into my lungs
to blow away
the ashes of houses forgotten

in the streets
the faces of the people
have to be picked up
from the ground they plaster

alien the native
a piece of meat
from which is bit
a self foreign to itself

FRANZ NABL

(1883–1974)

Loveable

In order to know and understand the city well, in its innermost essence, you would have to remember it from the time before the First World War when it was still the capital of the ›crown land‹ of Styria, right at the centre of old Austria and not beyond the pale as it is now, shunted off on some dead end branch line. Then, life still flowed through it in tireless circulation and was not forced to a stop or to turn back. There were language borders nearby then as well, but they were not the unscalable walls they are now. They were open borders, with unimpeded circulation flowing freely over them. Admittedly, even then the city was jokingly referred to as ›Pensionopolis,‹ a place of refuge, of peace and quiet for those who had arrived at the regulation age barrier or perhaps had got tired of serving the state or in the army a little early. Already by the end of the 18th century a few words of praise are to be found in a text, » … once here, most of the people who move to Graz lose the desire to pick up their walking staff and continue wander.« However, it doesn't necessarily follow that the proverbial ›stomach‹ love or the reputation that with a relatively modest income one might live comfortably, is responsible for tempting them into spending the evening of their lives here. It could be that other, more noble, reasons also played a part. Again and again one is tempted to compare Graz to a woman who is loveable and at the same time very motherly. That perhaps provides an answer to the question about the cause of its attraction. Beauty is certainly part of it, but it doesn't have to be conscious, provocative or recognised as such by every parasite of love at first glance, tempting him only to fleeting dalliance. It has to be such that it reveals itself only after a second or third glance and then only to reverential seekers.

That certainly does not mean that Graz does'nt possess any famous and valuable sights to be seen. Whoever has looked upwards at the ceremonial staircase to the mausoleum of Ferdinand II the virulent opponent of the Protestants, whether beneath a southern deep-blue summer sky or through the silver-shot veil of a moonlight night in winter will not be able to forget the picture so easily. That goes for the view of the provincial parliament too, although its beauty is not so immediately accessible to the casual stroller but to the seeker who proceeds through the gateway and then stands before the dancing row of arches which forms the Arkadenhof. And he would then be happy to loose himself in the cool, dim lanes of the old city, with their house walls and their sometimes outspread flying buttresses and their aged grey palaces. As with the provincial parliament, their often bare and undecorated facades lie wonderful stone arcades covered with leaves which wreath the courtyard.

Beauties like this do not cry out loud or ingratiatingly to be noticed and admired, they are sufficient unto themselves like attractive aristocratic women.

They feel unconsciously that the longed-for suitor intuits their existence behind the modest façade and knows how to find them. And the small mansions from the Middle Ages and vormärzlichen[*] times probably fare much the same. Built by gentlemen of rank and by citizens who aspired to prosperity they once stood outside the gates to the city. Nowadays, along with their gardens full of rustling trees they are imprisoned within its walls. Because the city still exercises its strongest magic through the landscape. It is not just surrounded by this extravagant abundance, the landscape penetrates the city, splits it open to its innermost house. It is victorious, triumphant on the throne of the Schlossberg which has become its symbol …

FRITZ VON HERZMANOVSKY-ORLANDO

(1877–1954)

Masked Ball

»Yes, yes, Graz,« Sreysand assuming the word again. »I know the city very well. There's not a lot happening there nowadays anymore. But back then! Did you know that Shakespeare directed a performance of »The Merchant of Venice« in Graz? He had to flee from Vienna after »Measure for Measure« because of

---

[*] vormärzlichen, lit. before March, i.e. before the 1848 revolutions

slandering the Chamber of Advocates, as every educated person knows. The metropolis' well-known xenophobia also contributed to that. No wonder. Vienna is the natural capital of the Balkans, I might even say it is the Mongolian gland of Europe.

PETER DANIEL WOLFKIND

(* 1937)

Graz

Whether it is in Prague, Krakow, Salzburg, Belgrade or London somewhere in all of these cities there is a fortress, a few ruined walls, an old royal castle. And each one of these fortresses has its story. And all of these stories are very similar: building, extension, siege, defence and destruction. And inside all the royal castles it looks very similar. A splendid public room, an armoury, walls and corridors, a wide four-poster bed in which a hero was procreated, born or stabbed, a chapel, a park. And in all of these cities there is a church of pilgrimage, a few monuments. And in all these cities there is an unassuming house somewhere where a famous poet, painter or composer was born. And in all of these cities there are a few dreamy old town streets, a monument to the plague and a few new buildings of various degrees of ugliness. And so, for me at least, all these cities melt into one city, into a model ›European City.‹ And so Graz is also one of these items of serial production on the conveyer belt of history made after the same model. And to salve the feeling of local patriots: a serial product with special features.

MAX BROD

(1884–1968)

Graz is like Zurich

(September 1911)

The little city (Zurich) is more elegant than Prague – banks spend a lot on their furnishings, everything in blue marble. The impression is of a flourishing and beautiful city with unremarkable inhabitants rushing around seemingly coincidentally between the wonderful buildings. One does not want to believe that they have created these beautiful things. Graz seemed to me to be similar.

GUSTAV SCHREINER

(1793–1872)

On Character

By the way, the character of the common Gratzer has certain features which give evidence of a mixture with Slavic elements. Slow working, acting with deliberation, he is averse to all things foreign and is not very obliging. Only when something is complete and perfect does it slowly win his acceptance. Great friendliness is not a trait he can call his own, he only decides to greet you with difficulty except when the person he encounters might influence his fate. Great cleanliness is not commonly found in the lower classes.

JÖRG-MARTIN WILLNAUER

(∗ 1957)

Geograffito

As always Graz comes
before Linz, Wels and Gols,
Enns, Gurk and Faak
Hall, Rust and Ried
Lech, Zell and Ybbs
Weiz and Wien
the finest four-letter town
in the word.

JOSEPH FREIHERR VON HAMMER-PURGSTALL

(1774–1856)

Magic Cauldron

Graz the magic cauldron! Who was it that wrought
making you into to a fairy region? ... Graz, densely
entwined with rose groves and water meadows
is a sparkling talisman.

BERND SCHMIDT

(∗ 1947)

Somehow, the Rain really is Different

When it rains in Graz it's certainly similar to how it
is in Vienna, Dunkirk or New Orleans, as it is in
Hamburg, London or Marburg on the Lahn. But in
Graz it's somehow just not the same.

Perhaps you could say the same from the point of
view of the other cities. But one thing is certain, in
Graz the rain is more unpleasant than in Vienna,
Dunkirk or New Orleans, in Hamburg, London or
Marburg on the Lahn.

The rain is unpleasant in Graz because we are in
Graz, in the rain.

The rain doesn't bother us if it's falling in Vienna,
Dunkirk or New Orleans, in Hamburg, London or
Marburg on the Lahn. It just shouldn't fall in Graz.

Except when we happen to be in Vienna, Dunkirk or New Orleans, in Hamburg, London or Marburg on the Lahn while it's raining in Graz. That's how we from Graz are.

ANGELA KRAUSS

(∗ 1950)

Graz

I hope I never allow myself to be carried away so that I pass judgement on Graz. Graz was home for me for a year after the Iron Curtain opened. Graz had to be everything I had imagined in the world behind the world in the Fifties, Sixties, Seventies and Eighties. And of course it was.

PETER ROSEGGER

(1843–1918)

Big City

Slowly the cost of food is rising because Graz is trying to give itself the face of a big city which, quite honestly, is most unbecoming.

HANNS KOREN

(1906–1985)

That's how it was meant to be from the beginning

The image of this city is typified by the masterpiece that is the Town Hall, the quiet beauty of the old castle, the exciting contrast of the gothic cathedral alongside the mausoleum with its southern character and by the many houses and palaces, as homes and for prestige, that the nobility and citizens assembled here in this province, in this city built for a serious purpose. Time and again the Italians provided the models for them, from Venice and Friaul. In addition to the children of the province, Slovenians from Lower Styria and Krain were employed within the walls. In the same way there was a matter-of-course mixture; in the »Mannschaftsbücher*« of the developing industry of the eighteenth and nineteenth century there are the German names of provincial farmer's sons alongside those from Slovenia and Italy. The latter are a testimonial, as is the image of the city, its origins and development, mirroring the function and meaning of this Inner Austrian metropolis. Its size was intended to serve not only its own small province but a region which stretched as far as the sea and was considered to be an integrated unit. What was thought

---

* List of employed persons

here in this city, what was achieved, sacrificed for, tolerated and, naturally, in a modest way, what was earned from all of this, applied to the larger region that stretched from Dachstein to the Adriatic in which the Germans in Styria and Karinthia along with the Slovenians around Krain and the Italians near Görz and Aquilea were all subject to the jurisdiction of a single regent. It applied to the unified region which has gone down in history under the name of Inner Austria but which, as a unity of intellect and traditional, has not disappeared from history. These borderers of the great peoples who constituted the Occident, the Latin, German and the Slavic peoples have lived together too long with an historic task, in an intellectual struggle, in economic reciprocity, under a legal and political administration.

In the centuries in which the concept of a transitional period from the sixteenth to the seventeenth century changed and, from a superficial viewpoint, appeared to dissolve, uncountable pathways of economic cooperation were nevertheless opened up. At the same time countless ties of personal friendship were confirmed through blood relationships and continually renewed, so that they have continued to be influential right up to the present. This period was unique and bound up with the European situation. If we define this space today, and especially today, as a space for responsibility, it is not simply a matter of reminiscence or the maintenance of a folkloric tradition. The are no privileges in this region anymore but rather a joint responsibility. Every person who considers that the desire for peace between nations is more than just a slogan can and must accept this responsibility for themselves. It is the first moral task our generation to seek it with all possible passion and energy, drawing on their experience of this century. Where else could they have begun this any earlier than there, where the rubble and weeds of misunderstandings and errors of generations need clearing from the pathways.

WALTHER VON DER VOGELWEIDE

(~1170–1230)

Oh woe to you, you riches!

I've been told from the Seine to the Mur
from the Po to the Trave I can see straight through
      their like:
Most care not how they acquire possessions,
if I have to acquire them like that then farewell
      wonderful feelings!
Possession were always pleasant, but esteem came
before ownership. But nowadays ownership is so
      esteemed
that it can sit with the king,
with all the lords of the king's council.
Oh woe to you, you riches! What will become of
      the Roman Empire!
You aren't great! You also have intercourse with shame.

JOHANN GOTTFRIED SEUME

(1763–1810)

Staying and Resting

Graz: I want to stay here a few days and rest; I like the city and the people. You know that the town lies pleasantly on both sides of the Mur; that the whole has an overall appearance of bonhomie and prosperity which is most comfortable.

Graz is one of the most beautiful large regions that I have seen up till now, the mountains round about present marvellous views and in the best season must have a superb effect.[*] The castle quite high up on a mountain can be seen from far away and from it you have a view of beautifully cultivated land, herded together marvellously by the rivers, mountains and a number of villages. As I got up there and went through the castle gateway there was a corporal standing there sunk in the act of whistling one of the best pieces from the opera »The Cracower,« the proximate cause leading to the outbreak of the revolution in Warsaw.

---

[*] Seume was in Graz in January

FRANZ GRILLPARZER

(1791–1872)

On the Way to Italy

Thursday morning dawned cold but nice. The Mürz valley, which in summer must be marvellous, stood leafless now and bare, still partly covered in snow. Two old knightly castles, the last one the family castle of the Stubenbergs.

Changed the route in Prugg and instead of going to Venice via Klagenfurt, to Trieste via Graz. The beauty of the Mur valley. The mountains take on a more preponderating character and are closer to those of Salzburg. One precipitous cliff over the left bank of the Mur is called the Virgin's Leap.

Graz, wonderful surroundings, gives the impression as you come from the mountains as if you came to peace after the war. The Schlossberg towers over it like a protector. The city is large, the streets narrow, the road surface bad. Harnessed the horse and left in the dark without stopping off.

JOSEPH KYSELAK

(1799–1831)

A Beautiful Chestnut Allée

In order to recuperate from this five-hour journey I chose the well-known Wild Man in Schmidtgasse. If there is a hostelry in a provincial city that the majority in residence consider deserving of praise, to be held up as a good example, then it is the Wild Man in Gratz. The good host and owner has basked in praise for so many years and this will continue as long as the stomachs and spirits of the guests are spiced with the cleanliness, good cooking, unadulterated drinks, lively service and splendid company at table. In addition the payment demanded for this select refreshment is small.

Graz's head, I refer to the Schlossberg, has lost its former countenance because of the bitter wounds of 1809 but the city has gained immeasurably in friendliness from its softened expression. The Grazer's citadel is gone but every single one of the inhabitants has constructed a fortress in their hearts that no enemy in the world could overcome. The only stonework on the wide summit of the hill apart from the round clock tower which the citizens had to pay to have spared by the French is a spacious cistern and is now used as a look-out post fire like St. Stephen's Cathedral in vienna.

A lovely avenue of chestnut trees leads us back to Graz again; but, looking back, it is not due to accept-

ing this gentle invitation that I feel nothing but gratitude to this unforgettable city and thereafter went
walking on the plain to Strassgang in good spirits.
There, on a little hill on the right, is the Church of the
Mercy of St. Florian. Before that the pilgrimage Chapel
of St. Peter and St. Paul looks majestically down on
the traveller from the highest point in the woods on
the right. Watched ad nauseam by holy halls like this,
it is with confidence that one dares to enter the woods
through which a good trail takes pilgrims to *Doppelbad*
in an hour.

KAREL HYNEK MÁCHA

(1810–1836)

Let's wait for the horrendous bill

3rd ... widely scattered ruins; we stopped there at
midday with a very mixed but nevertheless select
company. The doctor ate with the captain and his
wife. We sat at the table with two counts one of whom
had a wound on his leg. They were Hungarian. We
enjoyed the conversation. New *firearms*.

Hunters and jockeys in Magyar costumes. The
count offered us his coach. Then we ate. There was
a soup, meat with a sauce, beetroot and sauerkraut.
Rolls with salad and a good wine. And then someone
came along with rings on all the fingers of his left
hand and another with a small whip which just brushed

the captain. They didn't get any soup for a long time. After a time it emptied. We drove off as well. While the doctor gave the inkwell back we caught up with the counts. They drove in Magyar style, with three horses, sitting on the coachman's seat themselves, the lackeys in the coach. The doctor was of the opinion that it was Lichtenstein. Then we drove to Graz and looked at the city. At the market everyone looked at us strangely because of our unusual clothes. Then along comes the Count and I turn so that he wouldn't see us but he continues to come towards us, stops and makes a perfect bow. Then we looked for somewhere to spend the night. At the Florian, even with much persuasion and bowing we got nothing and it was the same at the Sandwirt. It was only at the Goldenen Adler that we managed to find a pleasant room. During the time the roast was prepared, the potatoes were boiled and the capons ran around in the courtyard, we waited for the horrendous bill. *Datum in nostra camera ad Aquilam auream die J. Sept. et nunc; Felici not te.*

4th. In the evening we ate potatoes with onions and the publican's wife told us how they had been fleeced in Mariazell, that she had to pay 53 and 24 florins for 3 days. For the goose she charged us 5 fl., for the room 6fl. and she still only came to 32fl. We went to bed ...

FRANZ GRILLPARZER

(1791–1872)

For a Friendship Book

(in November 1843)

I came in late November
to Graz, the homely town;
The year was old and weary,
And I was old and ailing.

It needed but two glances
from the sun, a gaze of fondness,
and for old November and I
Life and warmth came back again.

FRIEDRICH HEBBEL

(1813–1863)

Lodged at The Wild Man

Graz, 28th of June

At five we arrived in Graz and lodged at the Wild Man
which had been recommended. We got a room which
led out on to the so-called terrace which offered us a
view first of the hostelry garden, then of the botani-
cal garden and finally down an imposing avenue of

chestnut trees. By evening it had stopped raining and we took a walk through the city which is quite spread out. Since then the weather has been very inclement. On Sunday I went out alone and went into a church. At first it seemed to be like any other with its own half dozen Madonnas and pictures of Christ. As I neared the altar, however, I noticed that it had another exit which seemed to lead out into greenery. I wondered about the unusual view that met my eyes and I followed the people that were using this exit. I was surprised in a really delightful way. I stepped into a monastery courtyard in which peace itself seemed to have built a little home. An elongated rectangle lay before me, surrounded by a passage in which the little chapels and confessionals alternated with each other and on which the former monks' cells abutted. In the centre a chestnut tree strove upwards, one which was probably unequalled in the whole world. The branches stretched over the whole area like arms protecting it from the blistering heat of the sun as it did now with the rain which just wet the crown but could not penetrate it. Enough, it was a tree which gave me the impression of a living being and caused me to feel a great reverence. Next morning I took Tine there, the place and the tree provoked the same feeling in her and I felt I would be compelled to curse anyone who would harm it in any way, even if it was only a loose feather or a piece of stone. Of course that would not apply to the poor day labourer who carries out the execution with an axe but only the stolid holy Joes or civil servants that order it. In the evening we went to the theatre and saw Nestroy's »Schützling«[*] with himself in the leading role. The piece is not without merit and is certainly rounded as a whole, completely suited to making the audience forget that each of its three hours consists of sixty minutes. The public was plentiful and was not stingy with applause, I myself clapped heartily along with the others because I think that every lively effort within the circle of those on whom I also depend, is worth its money. Only something which is a complete nullification, an astonishing mass of importunate work with its deviously won success makes me angry. Of course, I cannot agree to call Nestroy, along with that lansquenet, Fritz Schwarzenberg, a modern Shakespeare, but I cannot deny his healthy natural and hard-working talent and have a higher estimate of him than most of those who circle him in Vienna on iambic stilts. By the way this was the theatre where, in my youth, I got my first reprimand for coming late: from the man who was in charge of and allocated the seats in the back stalls to be quite precise. However, I wasn't the only one he accused of coming just ten minutes before the beginning. He did the same with my wife and a number of other women with whom we were not acquainted ; the penalty commensurate with the guilt. That was Sunday, Monday went by in a most unpleasant way without us doing anything and without entertainment. Today, Tuesday, we climbed the Schlossberg without the slightest idea of the enjoyment that awaited us. I

---

[*] protégé

think that I have never seen such a view as that looking down from there. Thank God that the era of fortresses has passed, that the storage places for canons and mortars have been turned into gardens.

... We take great pleasure in the extraordinarily beautiful fruits, the strawberries and cherries, that are offered in such quantities and, for someone coming from Vienna, at such surprisingly cheap prices ...

ARTHUR SCHNITZLER

(1862–1931)

Diary, 1893

29/8 Klagenfurt- Graz. – Hilmteich. – Hartner. – Pichler. Letter from Fifi, false, pathetic. – From Gusti, who wrote to me, Mz. told her a dream in the morning ... 30/8 Graz. – Fechner. Pichler. Hartner. – Morning in Maria Trost. The praying convent girls who look at me and S.; the stupid pictures and sayings – the bird in the dome, rejoicing and chirping. – Nm. Bic. [with the bicycle] – Judendorf. – Riding: Pichler and Hartner ... 31/8 Semmering railway.

RICHARD WERTHER

(around 1900)

The Touching Naivety of Small-Town People

The omnibus rattled and roared over the cobbled drive up to Hotel X, one of the first inns in Graz, the charming alpine city that might be called a large city and a garden in the same breath. There is no city with streets so homely, such well-tended parks, green spaces with trees and expanses of meadow and such beautiful, charming young women as Graz. So it is no wonder that this city with so many sights and which is so pleasant is the oft-visited destination of many foreigners. This is even more so because it seems to have been created for the specific purpose of acting as the starting point of countless pleasant and rewarding parties for the upper Styrian mountains. It is joined by bustling activity in the streets, the people look at life so happily and in such a friendly way that every stranger is certain to feel a particular joy when he sees the laughing faces. In every other large city there is an industrious hustle and bustle, each trying to run the other down on the street; personified self-interest rules the day here. In Graz, in contrast, the active life of the big city is combined pleasantly with the comfortable, heartfelt naivety of the provincial town inhabitant and it is this that touches us in such a cosy and pleasant way.

JOACHIM RINGELNATZ

(1883–1934)

I drove to Graz

They really tested my mettle,
I went to Graz as if to battle,
But underway, I came from Wien,
I saw from afar alternating
Mountains of snow and mountains green.
I made rhymes while travelling
as consolation. I began to preen –
The snow melts,
and a valley melts.
And woods I saw and cows
And meadows of olive-tinted pelt.
I said to myself all the way to Graz:
Make an effort anyhow.
I came, I did, that's that.
When I turned into Rosenkranzgasse
(Known only to natives I'm sure)
A smart Grazer loser
– after the aforementioned battle
In the evening – won in the night
and both indisputable
so a victory like that was
made easy by the Grazer
who get in each other's hair.

(1901–1974)

I stood there and listened

Then the beautiful wooded valley full of green flowing water, southern rail, southern rail, in the direction
of Yugoslavia, friendly people so it's said and the foreigner doesn't notice anything to do with Tito, there
are supposed to be rocky islands there and the palace of the Emperor Diocletian but I get out before
that. I get out in a city with yellow houses and growing from the ramparts there are mighty old planes, a
former residence, now full of pensioners and pupils,
ancients and children and lately a little industry. I
know my way around here a little, I know the bridge
over the excited Mur, I know a few of the names of the
streets and squares and some of the sights as well, the
Schlossberg with its clock tower, the stairway in the
castle. The market too, with its opulent flowers and
the fruit from the south. There I stood and listened to
what was being said. So very softly, so very confiden-
tially they are talking about Angela Prokop, the Viennese prostitute murdered in Prater, by who, by her
pimp, no, not by him. She had a child and she worked
for the child, good job, during the day, by the way,
only during the day, she was in bed by eight every
evening, it's a good thing that she's dead, says a hard
woman's voice at the end. I didn't come here to find
out something about Angela Prokop, neither did I
come to read poetry in a seminary or eat peppers in

the Krebenkeller. Why did I come? Only to see your features in the faces of your relatives, to re-discover the sound of your voice in the sound of their voices, blood relatives, that's how you say it, and some things repeat themselves, the small head, the tones of laughter, the urbanity.

29th June

In Peter Handke's ›audience abuse‹ we were supposed to become aware of our existence and our present state of being and that was what we were provoked into doing from the stage. Our role as audience, as accomplices, should simply consist of that. In the footlights were the young men who announced their existence and present state of being in word and leaps. On the other side was the partly distraught, party amused audience that might have had something to say but didn't want to. For as long as there has been modern theatre, which means for centuries, we have been brought up to sit still nicely, to extinguish ourselves, to become all ears, all eyes and the darkness in the auditorium, more or less light on stage, all underlined how we were supposed to behave. No more Miss Soundso, no more Signor Taletale, those people are transformed into Antigone and Achilles, Grillparzer's Medea and Beckett's Hamm. It is supposed to be the end of all that, forever, possibly. Youth, babbling and cavorting musically dictated a new role for us. In that same harsh light, each person is himself, *remains* himself, becoming aware of his physical and mental state, his boils, his itching foot fungus, his adulterous or murderous wishes. The audience was addressed from the stage as a stall of invalids, to be screamed at through loudspeakers. In the end it was not so much different to previous occasions as some who had recognised themselves with a shudder in Richard the Third or Lady Macbeth though that had been under cover of darkness, independently and with less bossing around. Each had had their own experience, had it for themselves, which, here and now, is something that shouldn't happen anymore. We and you, we heard again and again, we funny, sad mop-heads, you depraved, hypocritical theatre-goers. Basically only the moment was supposed to bind us together, the time we lived through together between eight and ten p.m. That was not much, not much more than the appearance of a few jokers in a waiting room despite the brilliant verbal fireworks and the exact mimicry, all of us in the same room, under the same bright lights, breathing the same air, no more than that.

ROLF DIETER BRINKMANN

(1940–1975)

The Image of the Night Sweeper

Arches, passages, bent, narrow streets, at five past midnight far and wide nobody to be seen and no car traffic, on the edge of the scene a single street sweeper scraping a little back and forth, with a cart, sweeping alone here in the still of the night./ That was the only living motion I encountered here at that time.

The image of the single street sweeper at night proceeded to load itself up with meanings from all sides, for me they could not be overlooked because the street sweeper was always there quite concrete and his activity was equally concrete – the meaning came from the empty street that he swept, from the silence, the darkened houses, it arose from each single, short swing as he swept the dirt together – from the scrolls and curlicues round the dark windows, from the dusty paintwork of the next house and the parked car around which he swept – but none of it could be established unambiguously: what hours did he work, and when did he have breakfast? – He really did sweep alone, there were no others nearby. There was something completely senseless in the view: something horribly unnecessary as well and it was simultaneously ridiculous – a lone man sweeping things before him somewhere in the middle of a city …

When I got back to the hotel I remembered a welter of individual details from yesterday and today: that once again the whole affair had not been worth it, even financially in the light of the physical effort alone – an additional business. / The nasty game of the loutish, drunken people plus vanity. / A shamanistic litany about how sense is nonsense with sounds of children's rattles with a grumble as a counterpoint to the children's rattle. / Artmann, who holds his hand in front of a toothless mouth and wipes his mouth before he kisses a woman on the cheeks, was intended as funny, was serious though, because of bad breath?/ Dionysian? Rubbish! Pathetic. / The mechanical laughter of the people who read it as a subservient attitude, a whinnying, that was pushily, annoyingly loud especially from Schweizer with his already thinning hair combed onto his forehead. / Good: the insight that I don't even want to take a holiday in Austria.

My expenditure on Monday: midday meal 22 schillings[*] postcards 14 schillings, stamps and cigarettes 39.90 schillings, coffee 13 schillings, two films 42 schillings, evening meal 80 schillings = 235,90, about 35 DM.

Moments of inner fright at the piggish ways in Forum.

Recollecting my reading, it must have been strange, someone comes to the front, sits down, white shirt, tie, black jacket, dark grey trousers, begins to read quietly, the text hangs in the air and begins to turn, goes away again after 20 minutes without saying another word, sits down until the event is finished, off to one side and vanishes. What was that? A hieroglyph?

After the reading I was supposed to talk about my impressions, there was also an invitation to dinner involved but I saw it was going to be endless verbalisations again and preferred to eat alone and to pay for my own food, to entertain myself because that makes everything stronger and doesn't mean disap-

---

[*] Approx. 13.76 schillings to the Euro, postcards 35 schillings (you can get stamps at the tobacconists!)

pearing in a desert of backwards and forwards without results. (The chap from the radio told me how, as a student, Peter Handke broke with his father here, had no money and had dramatised Dostoyevsky's Crime and Punishment in 5 episodes as a form of dealing with the confrontation with his father. That must have been a challenge. Wow) ...

GERT F. JONKE

(* 1946)

That Time Before Graz

Empty room. Grotesque, ceremonial, solemn music.
a
thet tam
b
thet tam bevor graz
a
we werena suppost to git thur
b
tha sety, thet we werena supost ta gait ta no
a
tha sety, thet onlee existed in owr fantasee
b
tha sety, thet onlee existed in owr imajinaeshon
a
tha sety, thee ald barok howzes

b
tha rifer, thet thae maebe kalled tha mur
a
butt wee dinna no, bekuz we didna geat as fur us graz
b
how shood we no whot they call tha rifer
a
we hud to deepend on tha map
b
on tha naemz rit on tha map
a
but hooz ta sae thet theyr no tha rung naemz
b
but hooz ta sae whot tha reel naemz are
a
we wantud ta faynd owt tha reel naemz
b
to faynd owt tha reel names, we wud hav hud to geat ta

graz

a
but we didna geat ther
b
we'll niver geat ther
a
hooz goin ta tel us tha reel naemz
b
nobodee, bekuz weer too far awey
a
too far awey frum graz
b
thet tam
a
.thet tam bevor graz

b
tha sety, we couldna git a proper picshure of
a
we couldna iver git a proper picshure of it
b
bekoz we niver nyoo tha reel naemz
a
we didna iven no if tha naem »graz« was rite
b
it sed it wuz on tha map
a
but tha map
b
we werena aebel to git a proper picshure bekuz
it onlee eggisted in owr imajinaeshon
a
and eech one of us has anuther picshure of it
b
graz
a
thet tam bevor graz

(End of the ceremonial, solemn music such as »Last
Year in Marienbad« or »Hiroshima mon Amour«)

FRANZ WEINZETTL

(∗ 1955)

At the Other End of the Tunnel

»Were you ever in Graz?« (A frequent question amongst us children, just as later teachers would ask who had been to the sea.) Didn't every tunnel-building game imply, above all, that there was someone who had left behind what we dreamed Graz to be? Hopefully growing up would also mean that your own life would, little by little, reach that far.

My childhood fear of being at home alone. »Where he must feel safe,« I often heard it said, but safest of all I felt when I was in the open air. And a lucky day – one when you could still hear even the smallest sound from the place on the other side of the Kogel[*] – the piece of land where I grew up (and am still at home) rose, I breathed easier. My feeling of well-being was never greater that during this sort of weather though it made most people ill.

The meadow behind the house, letting go and ascending; how often have I wished for that?

And in the evening, on a clear starry night, the gaze upwards, once in a dream I dived upwards, I managed to swim free into that brightness. (»How are you down there in the rain?« someone asked two decades later on the telephone. I would rather have been up there, to have been in Graz, where the sun was shining.)

---

[*] An Austrian term for rounded, wooded mountain top.

The first time I went to Graz I was sick: Because I was going there too fast? After a stay in one hospital and then another. How intentionally did I run into the scythe, fall down the cellar stairs in order to get away to the city? No fairytale grotto railway ride, no visit to the city park. The long corridor down which my mother strode away. The strangers with loud voices, the pillow on my face getting heavier. Each time a scar as a ›souvenir‹.

When I was around twelve my father went with me one Sunday to not just any football ground but to the Graz Messe, somewhere I would go just one other time. I wanted to see everything but not take part in anything. I didn't feel like riding on the roundabout or on the bumper cars; my father tried to talk me into it with no avail. There were brochures sticking out of his jacket pocket. He would buy this and that, would be able to travel here and there. I promised him this once as a child.

And I wore my hair very long when, years later, I was in Graz with my mother who had my sympathy for the way people stared at me. I would never forget it, it was like a warning.

Where and when was I first happy in Graz? In the central park in the city, two months before I started my studies. There was almost no-one around. The blackbirds were lying in the grass like cats, their feather dresses unbuttoned. »The shadows of the tree trunks on the path seemed to me to be steps to something higher.« (I wrote down).

And in the evening from the little hills on the edge of the city – the lights down below, behind the picket fence, looking like sparklers as you walked by and when you stood still there was a fata morgana-like shimmer of a life I had longed for since childhood.

Down there for a long time afterwards though, extreme insecurity projected into the smallest corners of the city. In the tram, »the arm with the elbow leaning on the narrow window sill, and the hand closed in a fist, as if you were giving blood.« »Or I sat there as if I had a thermometer in each of my armpits.«

And always that wanderlust, just like it was in all the other places; not for another place, but for the place where I happened to be.

PETER GLASER

(* 1957)

Arrival in Graz

THE MACHINE FLEW in circles before landing at Amsterdam Airport and Glasser thought about whether it was love.

Is it a love of Graz? Every time he came back after months or a year he was wildly moved by the joy of seeing it again and every detail seemed worthy of embrace, every black number plate on a car with a G before the number, every tram stop, every uneven patch of tar on the street as if the special nature of the city shone out of it. How fabulous and piercing was the arrival when he was able to hear the city dialect over the taxi radio.

PIERRE VEILLETET

(∗ 1943)

One Night

Leaving Vienna as fast as I can
where I have endlessly dined
on boiling Kurtwaldheim broth
with mealy amnesia dumplings
on a low flame of irreconcilability

A long glide southward in the night
fake escape
helpless on the motorway
defenceless target of headlights
and there it is at last
the City of Graz – grace
a name like a prophesy
perhaps there hang
the hidden lamps of redemption

I came on the off-chance
but also without fear of this city
and think I hear
how Graz as greeting says
»My intentions are peaceful and
quiet, little Frenchman, but quiet
and a little tact, if I might suggest it.«

Little squares, like school playgrounds during break
in half shadow

high fronts, coloured like narcissus or jasmine
bundled, tightly ranked together
hold up the gaze, but not the day-dreams
behind the thick net curtains
heartfelt understanding lights up
a black silhouette swishes by
clerical
or more likely notarial
in any case conventional
A woman's profile at the window – is she reading or
                                                dreaming
without a glance outside – where is her life?
Is she one of the beautiful widows
who excite pity and desire
and what is it with this street
that she doesn't even cast a glance outside?
A sweet haze hovers over the cobbles
as if the dead beneath were too warm
houses like hot rolls
fresh from the oven
the bakery Edegger-Tax is dead smart
Can people who display
their croissants like jewellery
be malicious?
The more I look at it
the more I recognise this unknown city
where nothing hits you between the eyes
and apparently nothing coerces you either

Graz ›sticks out its chin‹ less than Salzburg,
is less trendy than Munich
is more reserved and less arrogant than Vienna

where the whole world is politely invited
to repeat everything briefly
as in an incorrectly named ›Spanish‹ Court Riding
School

And now I would like
to slip under the linen sheets
You have to sleep with a city
if you want to wake up
knowing the hidden reasons
why you made your bed here.

EVELYN SCHLAG

(∗ 1952)

Arriving

The station was full of students going on holiday;
grandmothers who were no longer allowed to choose
presents by themselves because they couldn't imagine what a Gameboy was, something that their grandson just had to have. Linda stretched her neck trying
to bring the platform number into her field of vision.
In a few minutes the inter-city ›Robert Stolz‹ would
arrive. She had never seen the paperback edition of
the HR letters. She had the bound version. It was icy
cold. A Pakistani held a bunch of roses under her
nose. She shook her head.

»I good, you good,« said the man. »You better good.«

At that moment a five minute delay was announced for the inter-city ›Robert Stolz.‹ She stared at the man.

»How much?«

»Three hundred schillings,« he said. She recognised Widmer as he alighted. He had the book in his hand and hung on to the carriage handgrip with two fingers while with the other he pulled his case after him. He was wearing a black beret over his grey hair and a camelhair-coloured winter coat.

»Ah,« he said and stretched the hand with the book towards Linda. »Roses?«

»For Frau Bartsch,« said Linda and took the roses in her other hand. Widmer stuck the book in his coat pocket. Then they greeted one another.

»On the way to Salzburg in the middle of nowhere we had to stop for a few minutes. Unidentified game path.«

»You'll thinks it's funny,« said Linda, »but on the West Motorway a couple of years ago a Thaya elk was …«

» … a what?«

» … run over. It had wandered from the Thaya[*] through Waldviertel[**] to Melk. Before the Iron Curtain came down it had survived in the death zone.«

Widmer pulled his scarf tighter around his throat. He coughed to one side.

---

[*] River in the north-east of Austria
[**] Literally: Woods Quarter, N.E. of Austria bordering on the Czech Republic

»In the dining car there was a draught,« he said, »it's not as cold at home as it is here. But the snow is lying.«

In the car Linda excused herself for having to put on the blower. Widmer wiped his steamed-up glasses with a paper handkerchief. The roses sat on his lap.

»Have you been in Graz often?«

»Yes, always in connection with HR. Many years ago I was supposed to help found the Nabl Institute. I don't know if you know the story. Apparently in June 1927 in Graz HR had a meal with Paula Grogger. One of the two of them must have had klach soup. I've been told that klach soup is consommé with a pig's trotter in it. A recipe in Paula Grogger's handwriting on the page of a calendar from Steirischen Haussegen[*] from the year 1927 that was found in Nabl's personal effects and is the only possible evidence for a relationship between HR and Nabl. In brackets below the title Klachl Soup is Hermann R:«

»Are there other possible R's?«

»As I said, I'm a bit sceptical which is why I declined the offer of a founder membership. But I ate the soup. I must say I didn't find it very agreeable. You know, the trotter sat in a grey broth …mmm.«

Widmer fell silent and buried his nose briefly in the roses.

»When I think of that trotter … I mean, a pig's trotter is something delicate, isn't it? The thing in my soup was much bigger. And despite its size it looked pitiful – as if some animal was in the process of sink-

---

[*] Lit. Styrian House Blessings

ing into a swamp and the trotter was a final, dumb cry for help.«

He looked at Linda sideways and blew his nose.

»I hope I didn't catch a cold after all.«

They were standing at a crossing. Linda stretched her back and looked over at Widmer. He had eyes that were almost black. Outside it was already dark.

»Was Paula Grogger a good cook?« she asked ...

GERHARD M. DIENES

(* 1953)

The Name

The Romans followed the so-called Alpine Slavs who created the Duchy of Carantanien. The names of quite a number of places and areas around Graz are Slavic in origin, such as Andritz (jendriza, rapidly flowing stream), Gösting (probably from gozd = mountain woods), the Ragnitz was a crayfish stream (raka = crayfish), contained in the name of the mountain chain Plabutsch are the personal names of Blagota and Graz itself refers to a castle (gradec = little castle) and probably from the Salzburg mission period (after 772 but before 828) to the Schlossberg itself, so-called by the Slovenian majority.

There is, however, a derivation for the name which comes from the world of fantasy but which stubbornly endures, it is the one which C. G. Ritter von Leitner put into verse in 1875 and printed in a book which was presented to all the participants in the 48th conference of natural scientists and doctors in Graz. Leitner presented the German guests with a Bajuvarian etymology for the name of Graz: in the long and distant past there were immigrants from the north who began to build a city on the Mur and, when asked what they aim of their action was said »G'räth's, so G'räth's!«[*] And thus happily the word ›Graz‹ came from many mouths; hurrah! And thus a Bavarian becomes a Styrian!«

Against the Turks

In many of the various publications on Graz, on city tours and other occasions it is still emphasised that the Turkish invasions turned the castle up on Schlossberg into the »outer defences of Christianity.«

Almost no mention is made of the enormous costs or of the Protestant aristocracy eliminated by the Catholic Habsburg princes. Neither is supposed to have had any influence on the fortress or its construction. The estates considered it would have been more sensible to invest in the extension of the fortress Kanischa which was under direct threat. More and more they regarded Schlossberg as a bastion directed against them (and thus against freedom of religion), exactly as the great majority of the Protestant citizenry did.

---

[*] If it succeeds, it'll succeed.

Usually it goes without saying that it was exactly during the period of that oft-cited threat that numerous castles and stately homes were built in the surrounding area. They lacked any defensive function but offered the nobility and rich citizenry a comfortable and recuperative life in the country.

In fact the Turks appeared before the city twice, in 1480 and 1532, without besieging it. Nevertheless, the consciousness of a Turkish threat remain alive for the people for two centuries. Historical research did not question this for a long time.

JOHANN CASPER RIESBECK

(1754–1786)

Nobody talks about anything except what belongs in kitchen or cellar

Their heads really are a part of their pot-bellies and are filled the same things – nothing but hams, sausages and similar items. Nobody talks about anything except what belongs in kitchen or cellar, with the exception of a few digressions to do with the theatre. The common folk differ from the orang-utans in few other things but the preparation of their food. I don't have to tell you that you must except the nobility and the officers from these two-legged animals without feathers. These also maintain an excellent table, as is customary in the province, but they attempt to feed to their intellect, although only with what otherwise normally serves as desert at a funeral breakfast.

ANONYMOUS

Here the General took up Quarters

Here they found the main square and Herrengasse occupied by a dense crowd, the crush was especially bad round the earl's Khevenhüller'schen house, now the earl's Wagensperg'schen house. Here was where Commander in Chief Napoleon had his quarters as the double guard of honour of Frenchmen and citizen's militia showed. Everyone was eager to see the famous general and no matter how much the crowd cursed Austria's implacable foe they admired his exceptional deeds.

JOSEPH CARL KINDERMANN

(1744–1801)

The French occupy the city

I conclude the history of this city with an event in the war against the French which has just ended which is as important as it is unexpected. One of the consequences of the agreed truce which took place in Judenburg on the 7th of April, 1797 was that the French should also take possession of this capital city. However, before that came to pass, the danger had already been recognised. Already by the 4th of April the Gubernium along with all the subsidiary princely and aristocratic authorities had been dissolved and on that very day the army High Command received the order to leave the city. Archive, treasury, supplies and depots including the (at that time) Austrian prisoners of war, the Mantuans and all those French prisoners of war to be found here and, finally, all political and other prisoners were taken away. A provisional provincial commission was set up with the permission of the royal court. It comprised 2 members of the clergy, 2 noblemen, 2 knights, and 14 citizens. The magistrate was granted more powers over an extended area and, by taking appropriate precautions and broadening the powers of armed citizens, made the best regulations towards maintaining law and order. Encouraged by this, many on the inhabitants (even the nobles) emigrated in considerable numbers. After the truce had been signed on the 10th April, the French moved in. That same night the French Commanding General Bonaparte, along with the general staff, took up quarters in the Stubenberg House in Herrengasse. All of this happened in good order, the French General even allowed the citizen's militia to occupy all the guardrooms and sentry posts along with his soldiers. This was to continue in the future and did so with punctilious exactitude until the French left. On April 12th Bonaparte left the city again in order to begin with the peace negotiations in Göss. After peace had been made, the greatest part of the French army retreated out of upper Styria through Graz: the first division arrived here on the 20th and the second two days later, both of them camped outside of Graz on the so-called Grazerfeld. On the 22nd Bonaparte came to Graz for the second time and the next day held a great revue of all the troops camped here. On the 26th the third division followed. From the 20th on, there was much tumult in Graz but everything came to an untroubled conclusion. Bonaparte left the city for the second and last time on the night between the 26th and the 27th April and the day after the third and final division left for lower Styria after Graz had been in the hands of the French for 18 days and happily suffered no damage except for a requisition which had been carried out for an insignificant amount of shoes and clothing. Within a few weeks after the French withdrawal everything was as it had been before.

STEPHAN BENDITSCH

(around 1790)

The Poor of the City

The one thing I must remark on is this, the city poor who are so richly blessed with children, first suckle on the poor and ailing breast and are then fed on the famous milk-sops [usually a goo of warmed milk and flour] from which they get huge stomachs, big heads and thin limbs. They often die off prematurely or become cripples and not infrequently increase the numbers of popular poor as annoying ›bread eaters‹.

On Culinary Pleasures:
All foreigners who look around the region and all those who describe their journeys agree the Styrians in general and the Grazers in particular eat much and well. We cannot and should not refute this legend completely. Even the most common citizen is in the habit of eating 3 or 4 dishes at midday ... A good soup, good, fresh beef, a well-prepared side dish of vegetables and seldom without a roast. it is served with bread every day. Wine or beer are a permanent accompaniment. The evening meal generally has one course less. Breakfast elevenses (sandwiches) are obligatory ...Even though our philosophy of life is not satisfied by eating well and much, it is still certain that the stomach is the first idol of animal life, the source of much good and evil. When the stomach is full we are happy, satisfied, quiet, obedient, it tames our desires, limits our vain strivings and we feel lucky in ourselves and at times something like blissful happiness. On the other hand an unsatisfied stomach can bring whole nations to revolt, defeats the greatest armies and pushes entire peoples out of their homeland.

ARCHDUKE JOHANN OF AUSTRIA

(1782–1859)

The Magistrate does not have the best of reputations

If you pay any attention to the voice of the people, the magistrate in the capital city of Graz does not have the best of reputations. The mayor is not competent enough to fill this post, his transfer to some judicial function or other would be best and it needs an energetic, powerful, upright man to clear up the Augean stables there instead. There is really no other choice available here except to look within the body of better regional civil service officials since the Magistrates Committee is useless in this respect.

Everyone is mistrustful, dissatisfied, anxious and worried about the future, no-one trusts anyone because he does not know if he is not talking to a police spy ... Even though I don't circulate much among people, many come to me and I hear enough to convince me more every day of how everything is going downhill. Maliciousness, fear, mean-mindedness, all of this increases daily so I don't have time to talk of anything else except hunting, fishing, eating, plants, machines otherwise you rub everyone up the wrong way and run the danger of encountering someone who will twist your words.

ANDREA WOLFMAYR

(* 1953)

The GRAZ Wanderer

... I've seen how the moon rose above the city and how the green and sky blue slowly became a dark blue heaven with a yellow disc and, in the end the city slowly began to light up, to glimmer like the stars in the sky ... it might just be that I've had a little too much of that divine apple wine ...

A phenomenal view, really. We're much higher than *Burg Gösting*, looking over towards it, indeed can almost look down on it, unbelievable that we decided to do this out of the blue on a simple summer morning! So, here we stand, sweating and looking, feet covered in blisters, at the surrounding Styria. From here you can see right to the *Gleichenberg Kogeln*[*] and to *Riegersburg* and down there lies the city spread out as if on a table cloth, like in the cinema or from an aeroplane. The red roofs round the Schlossberg, the churches, the Mur, the high-rises ...

Earlier there was a *cable car* here we're told, straight as a die it went, right to the top but there was an accident sometime and then they razed it. Shame. We definitely should go to the weather station up there. It's the old weather station, as you can see, all the instruments are gone, instead there's a modern radio

---

[*] Kogeln = rounded, wooded mountain tops.

station with utopian dishes and antennas right over there on the neighbouring hill, all shiny aluminium and much bigger. But we should take a look up there, it's worth it. So, grit your teeth, the extra few steps won't make that much difference. There is supposed to be a quite interesting memorial plaque there in Latin. »It doesn't matter,« he says boastfully to the gentleman with the information, »she can read Latin …!« That's right. Only she can hardly walk any more …

The plaque turns out not to be in Latin but in a undecodable German. Absurd the things some of our Grazer regional poets have done! Despite its length I don't want to withhold the text from you:

> On this spot
> on 30 June 1830
> J.J.M.M.
> Emperor Franz and Caroline
> Marie Luise of Parma
> SE k.k.Highness
> Archduke Johann and
> SE Serene Highness
> the Duke of Reichstadt
> stood inspired by the view
> of nature and the same
> feelings of thankfulness and
> and made the place holy
> where once did stand
> the king
> and the folks of Eggenberg and Gösling
> offered their hand

to this the consort of their love
so posterity would understand
their joy in memory.
and what had pleased the Emperor's eye
the western view
immovable and unoccupied
and wanderers in later times
should pause here from their climb
and drink the beauty from on high ...

HEINRICH LAUBE

(1806–1884)

Fried Chicken and Pints

I don't know what to tell you is typical for Graz except
that the provincial noble, the so-called cavalier, still
plays a paramount role as a hero here, that you can
see a lot of crucifixes and that on my way home at
night I looked for the city somewhere other than
where it was. Despite the fact that I lost my way and
got home very late the bar in my guest-house was still
busy. Fried chicken was still being ›gobbled‹ and
pints ›sunk.‹ The fried chickens are well known as
the centre of Austrian national identity. It's an historical mistake that the Austrians don't have a fried
chicken in their coat of arms.

JAROSLAV HAŠEK

(1883–1923)

The Captain and his Orderly

In 1912 there was a trial in Graz in which a captain who had killed his orderly played an important role. At the time the captain was found not guilty because he had only done it twice. According to the opinion of these gentlemen, an orderly's life is worthless. He is only an object, in most cases a whipping boy, a slave, a jack of all trades. No wonder, therefore, that a post like that, in the service of officers, demands cleverness and slyness. On the whole planet, his job can only be compared to the suffering of trainee waiters who, throughout history, have always been trained to diligence by slaps in the face and kicks in the pants.

PETER ROSEGGER

(1843–1918)

A Nuisance for the Censors

For twenty-five years now I, a moderate writer, have been fighting a power in Graz which I cannot hope to subdue but which is too weak to defeat me. It is the police apparatus. Despite the personal goodwill influential civil servants appear to show me, the continuous threat from their power has become a nightmare. My humorous lectures could have developed immediacy, liveliness and amusement in Graz, as they did in other places in Austria and Germany, if the police, who have to see every line intended as part of a lecture in this city, did not suffocate on every breath of fresh air. Pieces which already been censored and read publicly have to be submitted to be recensored yet again before the twenty-first lecture. I don't know what I have done to earn the distrust of the officials, since between honest people an oral or written assurance that the lecturer has not done anything improper with his manuscript since the last time it was censored should be enough. Indeed, a Grazer police officer ingenuously explained to me that I had done nothing personally or as a writer to cause mistrust. But still.

Unfortunately at this point in time it is not a matter of examples of the words or sentences (I wrote then in »Heimgarten«) of what the Grazer censor struck out. I can only give an assurance that my astonishment was such that I was sometimes speechless. But was the Censor correct in law? It was only retrospectively that the question arose as to why the Censor in Vienna, Prague, Innsbruck etc. did not hold to the same interpretation of the law. Not even one word was excised in these places and with the exception of two or three times in Vienna I was never required to lay my lecture manuscript before the Censor anywhere else. Where I have the choice of eighty lectures for other places in Graz I am allowed to read but twenty in which nothing has been cut out or, having been submitted, completely suppressed. I had thought that in Graz I would have an audience which was as well educated as in other cities. I am very well aware myself that a lecturer has more responsibility in front of an uneducated audience. But even in that case the police paid no attention to my programme when I lectured in Vienna once before fifteen hundred fiery social democrats and the proceeding were perfectly respectable. I am quite happy to admit that very often the things that are cut by the Censor are minor, that their loss endangered the whole as little as their presence but what hurts us as free men, authors and lecturers, indeed at times outrages us, are arbitrary impositions where the subject naturally knows more and has more tact about the subject than all but one in a hundred of those carrying out their duties. They are normally police officers with little leaning to poetry.

How incomparably uninhibited and fresh the »Heimgarten« could have been if the censor demon was not sitting on his shoulder like a lump of lead. The seven confiscations which have happened since its inception have taught me where, in Graz, the borders lie between what one is allowed to say and what you had better keep to yourself. The latter is certainly the larger and better part. It is neither the confiscations themselves nor the associated trouble and expense that are the worst things, it is much more the pressure and self-consciousness during the creative process. How far can one go in order to present the subject to the public in a way that approximates what one has to say. If there is one word which is not chosen with sufficient care or is not diplomatic enough, then the completed issue is confiscated and the whole article in which the inept or ingenuous word appears is ripped out to be pulped by prisoners.

One can, of course, appeal. But why? To enforce your rights under the law? In any case, the law itself is seldom dubious. In order to have the confiscated issue returned? That wouldn't be much use because the new issue should have been already been produced. Censorship is not just directed towards preventing the distribution of unwanted writings, but also towards harming the author or his publishing house. On the other hand this damage is not intended as a punishment because as such it lacks certain characteristics especially that of proportionality e.g. here a small infringement of press law answered with the removal of eighty thousand copies, there a serious infringement with the confiscation of a few exemplars which are discovered coincidentally. With that it's finished. A legal retribution however, has to be proportional to the size of the crime. The censor in Graz, though, is wont to hold back only those pages of a copy which contain the article to which exception is taken. But the issue is torn just the same and, due to leaving out of the misdeed, must be printed and bound again. Nevertheless, one is not being »punished,« it is just that something is being taken away from you.

By the way, I have become stricter and more conscious of any rules of proportionality – without defiance or bitterness. It is understandable that under pressure like this our authors are not able to develop a free artistic style and that the manly honestly of the writer can only come to fruition with the greatest difficulty. What grows is a quiet self-imposed lightness of step, the ambiguity of moral cowardliness and a reading-between-the-linesism – an underhandedness which can only be overcome with difficulty and only by those who consider their profession more important than everything else. No wonder writers envy their colleagues elsewhere in the kingdom or, wanting to have it equally good, come to the point when one or the other packs their bags and emigrates. »That's no loss,« I hear it said by those who believe that laws of censorship like this are necessary for their protection.

By God, I wouldn't dream of claiming special rights for myself like someone who doesn't know any better. However, I live under the impression that other papers enjoy a disproportional amount of freedom although even that leaves a lot to be desired. I'm very happy that the clericals (and the social democrats as well) are allowed to speak what's on their mind. They don't hurt the state thereby and bring life and progress to their readership. Why is the »Heimgarten« not allowed to reflect the authors' love of life (such candid words) to the same degree? If we can't obtain our rights per se, then we at least insist on equal rights!

Over the years the »Heimgarten« has, unfortunately, become very tame. It doesn't dare to print e.g. the sayings of Emperor Joseph II, or to assert in a humorous ditty that there are pious people who preach fasting while they sit at a feast or to use the words »Holy Joe« in the nicest possible way or to call God colloquially »Dad.« It doesn't dare to do that or to complain about insecurity in Graz, because the police feel themselves attacked by it. It doesn't dare to apply the fundamental Christian principle of peace and indulgence recently propagated by Tolstoy with regard to the militaristic states or to bring the human side of Jesus' glorious personality closer to us. »Heimgarten« doesn't dare to do that any more because it has had some bad experience with things of a similar nature.

Imagine what would happen if you wanted to aspire to even more important ideas! Each of my works which are regarded as being superior to The »Schriften der Waldschulmeisters,« »Der Gottsucher,« »Jakob der Letze«, »Das Ewige Licht« and others would not have been allowed to appear in »Heimgarten,« and, should the same spirit still rule, they would have been suppressed or at best have been released only after being subjected to many mutilations. A few of the pieces mentioned have appeared in »Heimgarten« but with much omitted and much watered down.

Now, in some circumstances that would be no great loss. But how would it have been if Anzengruber, Grillparzer or even Goethe and Schiller had had the luck to live and create in the conditions which prevail in Graz? And that is particularly so with Klopstock who is known as the holy singer! How did this man deal with dogma? No, no, Whatever was permitted in Germany *before* the revolution is scorned by us *afterwards*. That's how far ahead we are.

ERNST FISCHER

(1899–1972)

Homecoming

...On Sunday between 12 and 1 the uniformed students in their colours, well-ordered in row and column, marched round the Ring, the Goths, Alemannen, Vandals, Cheruskans, Lombards and whatever else they're called, the duelling societies. Their heads destined to wear coloured caps, their faces to be crisscrossed by sabre cuts and the carefully tended scars of ›honorable‹ duels. Now and then one of them would step up to a civilian and look at him straight in the eye: »Sir, you were staring at me. Will you give me satisfaction?« I don't know whether some primeval fear of the evil eye was hidden in this »stare« or just the disquiet of Germanic latecomers who were secretly afraid of being looked at disapprovingly by those nations who beat them to it; but in any case it was advisable either to deliver him a slap or to prove the inability of a non-academic to give satisfaction.

It was in a duel such as this that the young Alexander von Sacher-Masoch was wounded. In a state of semi-consciousness he heard only »Where is the ear? Where the devil has it got to? The ear, the chopped-off ear!« In the end the opponent's ear which Sacher-Masoch had chopped off was found under a cupboard. It was so covered in dust that it had to be cleaned with alcohol before it was returned to its owner. Even

116

though it had fallen into so much dust, it grew on again underneath the coloured cap of the affected part of the body. Even then I considered the mixture of dust and a chopped-off lobe of flesh as being symptomatic.

… The ancient jealousy directed at Vienna by this German nationalist city just ›round the corner‹ was made more overbearing by the fact that Austria had shrunk to an alpine country. Camped all around the Schlossberg, protected by the square clock tower with its gigantic faces and the round bell-tower with its huge bell, the »Liesl,« the sleeping city snarls. Ghostly figures steal through its sleep, absurdly strange strangers, broken talents, failed characters.

At school we learned that the trusty Bavarians, worn out from migrating, stuck their swords in the ground and reached for the spade with the earthy call »G'rät's so g'rät's!«[*] So it was just by chance that they settled; from the »g'rät's« came Grätz and finally, in enlightened times, Graz. So we should praise the industry, the rectitude, the success as a Bavarian inheritance and treat the reprehensible as a residue from the long lost original inhabitants. Besides that we mustn't forget that the town hall in Herrengasse is, with its gently curved façade and its arched courtyard, one of the most beautiful Renaissance buildings I know, as if a cloudburst from Toscana had deposited this mirage here. At any rate Nestroy died in this city.

---

[*] What turns out well, turns out well.

»Napoleon, who was the archenemy, but who anyway
...« With this, the local civil servant familiar with
regional history, discretely indicates that he of whom
he spoke was a great person and even the son-in-law
of the Kaiser. »Napoleon said in honour of our city –
La ville des graces au bord de l'amour! You know
what I mean, Graz on the banks of the Mur, becomes
remodelled into the graceful city on the banks of love,
by way of a Gallic play on words.« ...

JOSEPH ROTH

(1894–1939)

The hot chestnut salesmen who sing
»Gott erhalte«

I should also like to add that only in this crazy Europe
of nation states and nationalisms does the obvious
seem remarkable. Admittedly it is the Slovenes, the
Poles and Galicians from Ruthenia, the kaftan-clad
Jews from Boryslaw, the horse traders from the Bacska,
the Moslems from Sarajevo, the chestnut roasters
from Mostar who sing our national anthem, ›Gott
erhalte‹. But the German students from Brünn and
Eger, the dentists, barbers' assistants, pharmacists
and art photographers from Linz, Graz, and Knittelfeld, the goitred creatures from the Alpine valleys,
they all sing ›Die Wacht am Rhein‹. Austria will perish at the hands of the Nibelungen fantasy, gentle-

man! Austria's essence is not to be central, but peripheral. Austria is not to be found in the Alps, where you can find edelweiss, chamois and gentians but never a trace of the double eagle. The body politic of Austria is nourished and constantly replenished from the Crown Lands.

RICHARD ZACH

(1919–1943)

Unemployed

Unemployed on the river
We always sit on the same benches,
paid off and unemployed,
and let the sun shine into our empty stomachs,
the river quietly pushes its dirty waves before it.
You shouldn't stare at the brown bubbles too long,
or the river will rise in your brain.

LUDWIG BIRÓ

(1898–1972)

The Jewish community in Graz, 1938

The microcosm of Graz's small Jewish community exhibited all the strengths and conditions which were to be found everywhere in these times of great world revolution – the greatest since the great revolution in France. It showed the collapse of a world that had become unstable and insecure in the face of the first onslaught of new social and ideological ideas triggered off by the first World War which would, however, end in this war and would fundamentally change the social and political face of the earth. It is impossible to imagine that after the end of this great conflict between the three great systems of human organisation, liberalism, fascism and socialism, everything will be like it was before. Impossible to imagine that one is a house owner, businessman, industrialist or lawyer thanks to inherited wealth or lucky speculation or even just thanks to better elbows or a better education paid for by father. Impossible to image that money is the key to power, security and the humane enjoyment of life; that politics is nothing more than another way of doing business; that it is natural and right than one works and the other profits; that one person eats margarine and the other butter; that one person lives in three rooms while another shares his room with three others; that all of this has nothing to do with a higher power or special effort but simply because of money. The Jews, who were in the main »middle-class emigrants« and, in so far as they come from central Europe, brought with them the illusion that everything would be like it was. When not in Europe then in Erez. Within their own, dominant, form of Zionism from this generation of expellees. In Europe they have been persecuted and destroyed by exactly those groups they had joined in order to maintain prevailing social conditions, the middle class, the salesmen, tradesmen, lawyers and other academics with whom they were in competition. They believed they would be allowed to fight for privilege and overlooked the fact that only »equal rights for all,« only absolute justice and humane conduct could have secured their self-elected minority position. Any deviation from this line could be disastrous at some point. The economic egotism they were wedded to by their feelings of superiority in this area could take another form at any time. Then they would only be victims for others. Strangely enough they saw none of this, replete with possessions, conscious of their power and egocentric as they were.

GERALD SZYSZKOWITZ

(* 1938)

Before the Anschluss

The chief editor had called her and said, as he put down the telephone and continued to gnaw on his apple, that colleagues in Graz were talking about a *Volkserhebung** in their city.

Thousands of National Socialists had occupied the main square in Graz one hour before the announced Chancellor's speech and had forced Mayor Hans Schmidt (who himself was a someone who had been driven out of his home country in today's Yugoslavian Lower Styria) to hoist the Swastika flag over the town hall. The illegal Nazis had then torn the official flag up and has sung the Horst Wessel song instead of the national anthem.

The chief editor leaned back and gnawed dreamily on his apple.

»Report on page four. With picture.«

He scanned an agency report which the secretary had brought in. Then he looked again at Marianne.

»The economic indicators are reacting normally – fear-provoked withdrawals at the banks, cancellations from foreign companies. Tell me, dear lady, couldn't you go down to Graz? You must certainly know,« he said, »some illegals down there?«

»Me? No. Only father. And he certainly won't have time. It's his birthday soon.«

---

* a peoples' rising.

122

Her boss looked at her in amazement. Puntigam was always good for something new. She comes from a nationalist family, does she? And still works for the newspaper here? She's twenty-eight, she said so yesterday. What was her first name? Nordic or biblical? ...

... »You're going, Marianne, immediately.«

She didn't like it at all when the boss looked at her, sizing her up.«

»And begin the story with the fact that there has always been a thousand little clashes between the Germans and the Slovenians in Lower Styria and possibly it is exactly because of this that rowdy students of Graz (as every Jew knows) were the first in the Monarchy to preach a radically right-wing pan-Germanism. Write that nowhere else but in Graz is this delayed-puberty mucking around with sabre cuts on the cheek in *duelling societies* so popular ...«

»But ...«

»Nowhere but there is the sabre cut on the cheek the real mark of those who consider themselves part of high society. So, get down there, Marianne, and they won't make investigations that difficult for you because since the last amnesty you can see the illegals all over the place in public, in *Café Promenade* and un *Café Europa* all round Rintelen and Dadieu.«

The young Anglo-elegant Professor Dadieu, the subsequent gauleiter of the Styrian region, was the darling of the Grazer and called lovingly *Lindi* because of his remarkable resemblance to Lindenbergh of trans-Atlantic flight fame something Marianne was able to register on her first night. Dadieu was not only blonde like Lindenbergh and loved the newest and most precise flying machine like the American, he exuded a specially Nordic, north German self-confidence, especially today, because Minister Seyss-Inquart was a guest in his house in Merangasse and for that reason he had invited a whole succession of well-known Grazer figures.

There were rumours flying about between Herrengasse and Sporgasse that there was going to be a celebration the likes of which had never been seen in the city before.

He has also invited old Puntigam and, as Marianne drove with her father into the Leonhard Quarter on this first of March it was just after the sun had gone down and with the mild air wafting over from Stadtpark. Serious Merangasse got a little of the light-heartedness of Triest. They saw every street corner was occupied by SA people, that SS men in uniform had taken over the role of the absent police force and that there was a security cordon all around the outside of Professor Dadieu's house.

As Marianne and old Puntigam were undergoing a check, the men all round them set fire to their torches which presented a beautiful and exciting picture because the flames jumped like wildfire from man to man the whole length of Merangasse.

Even before the meal, while drinking a *martini Venezia* upstairs in the Victorian room, Marianne observed out of a window how the torch bearers stationed themselves on the corners in groups and then the spectacle began. The men marched in step, in rows of ten across the whole width of the street all in their so-called SA uniform with various different riding breeches and boots, but all in brown shirts with the same shoulder-straps and leather belts and singing enthusiastically about *comrades who shot the red brigades and reactionaries*. After five minutes Dadieu threw open the window as if he had been hard put to wait so long. He leant far out of the window and greeted those below pointedly with the Nazi salute so that even the furthest away could see it.

Dadieu, at present still the people's political editor at the *Vaterländische Front* was practicing here for a quite different post in the future and the men were filled with enthusiasm. Minister Seyss-Inquart stood a little behind Dadieu in the shadow of the curtain, tense and serious as if waiting here to make his entrance. The enthusiastic men below shouted »Heil Hitler,« again and again. »Heil Deutschland and Seyss-Inquart,« they shouted and marched past in a kind of goose-step as if they were not here in Merangasse, but *Unter den Linden* in Berlin.

As the men began to sing the Horst Wessel Song again a little later, Seyss-Inquart could not hold himself back and, at the words comrades, *the red front and reactionaries shot*, strode briskly forward to stand at the side of his host and he, the minister, also lifted his arm with the *salute of the future*. A howl of triumph greeted him from the street, but none of those down there stopped, none reacted privately and the secret army carried on past their secret leader. Some of the SA men went by for the second and third time. Right up to the end of the parade Seyss-Inquart stood there, erect, with his arm still raised in the Nazi salute and the flickering light of the passing torches played like lightning on his excited face.

For a few minutes Marianne was fascinated by the parade because she realised that it was not for nothing that the men of Styria – courageous but rough – had been soldiers down the centuries, borderers in the extreme south-east frontier area of the kingdom. These were men who took pleasure in laying into someone, who made short work of someone and who were born valuing life little, their own and that of others but then she started to feel afraid as she became conscious just how completely the Nazis had succeeded in drumming up this old border instinct. True, the beatings and stabbings were still only in song but those possessed dervishes down there made it quite clear to the Grazer – the new Koran was Mein Kampf, and Munich was the new Mecca!

Now she understood better why the Wagnerian Siegfried was so popular here in Styria – he too never discussed things, he reached for the sword.

Suddenly she saw her father alongside the erect Seyss-Inquart, also with his arm up-raised and, in a childish up-welling of love, she pulled him violently away from the window and pushed him into the next room, the library, which was in darkness but where the reflection of the torches wavered even more clearly than in the salon.

They sat down in two deep leather armchairs and looked at each other tensely. The old man had taken off his Styrian costume jacket and sat there in shirt sleeves. Old Puntigam knew what his daughter was thinking but was still visibly enjoying the evening. He was even perspiring in pleasure. For him, the all-enveloping belief in the future blended together with the prospect of beginning the greater-German banquet with a creamed »Schöberl« soup.

He had put himself in the picture and had perused the menu itself in the cloakroom, including the *Königsberger Meat Balls* which he couldn't imagine at all. Now he lit up a cigar with pleasure as if he could only assert himself against the power bubbling up outside on the street with a studied slowness. He looked at his daughter with satisfaction. It was a gift of fate, he thought, that his little Marianne could enjoy this decisive, historical moment together with him. He knew, of course, that she didn't believe in Nazis, but all of them together – the countless numbers of German men and women from Königsberg in East Prussia to Cilli in Lower Styria – would convince her over the next few years that it is easier to feed a mighty realm than the appendix of a country that this *Schuschnigg Austria* was.

127

»You should be congratulating us,« he said. What a misunderstanding, she thought and tried to hold on to the last remains of the sense of family togetherness.

»We should leave,« she said. »To our greater German future,« he said, and raised his glass ...

HANS KLOEPFER

(1867–1944)

City of the Volkserhebung

The enormous waves in our times have taken the people of Graz to the height of their destiny. As in the other Austrian provinces, under the pressure from the hated system of government, fronts of ›illegals‹ formed extending into the most insignificant mountain valley. They were locked in a continuous battle with the creeping encroachment of an informer state, helpless in the face of arbitrary and unscrupulous judicial acts and, fired on by an unshakable belief in the Führer, they held themselves in readiness for the approaching breakthrough to the longed-for Anschluss ... it was in that hour in world history that, for its ecstatic effort, Graz was given the name of honour – »City of the Volkserhebung«[*] and under the eyes and the care of the Führer now looks towards a future which, from the point of view of destiny, beauty and loyalty, it so richly deserves.

[*] Popular Uprising

DAVID HERZOG

(1869–1946)

The Burning of the Temple in Graz
on Reichskristallnacht

Then I was driven onto the street and told to run.
Since I couldn't run very well as a 70 year old psy-
chically broken man, I was encouraged with kicks.
The result was that I fell down right away and seriously injured both my knees. We came to the bridge
over the Mur. 3 of the fellows wanted to throw me in
the river but 2 women who wanted to watch the temple burning down shouted [«] You wouldn't really
throw the old man into the water in the middle of winter[«]. So they chased me along to the burning temple There was a pyre there for me. But at Rosenkranzgasse there were policemen standing watch and
[they] did not let anyone pass. Later I found out why.
It was intended to stop people from showing their
outrage in a fit of weakness and preventing other
events. Another version that was communicated to me
was (and this is the real one) that the fire brigade had
orders to protect the houses next to the temple, something which would have been very difficult if there
had been a crowd and [that is why] no-one could be
allowed to pass. That those who were allowed to get
to the scene were not able to dance around my charred
body can only be attributed to that fact. Then I was
driven to Griesplatz No. 2. There was a car waiting for
us in front of it, but before I could be put into it, the

bandits surrounded me and asked me the addresses of the other rabbis, civil servants and this is most significant, of the rich Jews. I told them I didn't know the addresses, because I never bothered with them. The criminal who had hit me on the nose yanked the right hand side my beard so that he tore out half it, causing terrible pain and making me bleed heavily. One of the others asked me where the Jew Koppel lived although he had died long ago, to which I answered that he lived in so and so street. At that the young rascal shouted [«] You Judas [«] at me. Somebody shouted [«] Shut up! [«] at him. Then they said to me that I wanted to give them 10 schillings, didn't I. I said [«] I don't have any money with me, [«] because I seldom carried any. At that they lifted me into the car that was standing in front of Griesplatz 2 already waiting to carry me off and then two of them got in with me and I was in the middle. I don't think there's any language like German for the number of nasty swear-words and they were all underlined by heavy blows. All of these were thrown at me. Murderer, robber, Jewish swine, vampire, bloodsucker and who knows what all. [«]We'll show you not to have money with you. [«] They took me to my flat. One of them went up to my wife who had a violent shivering fit and shouted that she should open up and when she did he demanded the 10 schillings. Luckily my wife still had 10S. and she gave it to him. Who knows what they would have done to me if they hadn't got the 10S! Then he came back down and told the driver to take me to the Jewish cemetery. We drove over the Radetzky-brücke and there, for the first time, I saw the temple lit up by the blaze, I cried dreadfully and the murderous youths shouted at me [«] Let's see if you're Jehovah can help you now, you murderer, you robber, you ruffian. Just see how your Jehovah burns! [«] And then my ears were boxed, I was pelted with blows, my hair was pulled. I mention it again – it was only at this point that I saw my much-loved temple burning brightly in the flames. because the first time that the drove me over the bridge with blows I couldn't look. When I saw my much-loved temple burning, I broke down sobbing that I would have thought would have moved stones to compassion. But the beast just shouted at me and said [«] Just look how the Jewish swine cries[«] and rocked backwards and forwards while hitting me. The driver, I'll never forget him, he was a bespectacled rogue of about 50, backed them up saying that whatever you did to vermin and riff-raff it was much too little. They should be killed in cold blood. And it was like that the whole way. And now we arrived at the Jewish cemetery and they said to me [«] Now you can dig your own grave and you should say your last prayer to your dirty Jehovah. [«] But the cemetery hall was locked and they didn't know that the porter lived at the other side of the grounds. So now they heldd a consultation as to what to do with me. After a secretive discussion they entrusted the driver with the duty to take me away and so we drove on further until we came to a field with haystacks. There they asked the driver what he was due and he said .[«] 8S. .[«]. They gave him the 10S. note and he gave them 2S. change. They threw it in my face and shouted .[«] Just so you can't say we took your money, you Jew.[«] I was forced to pick up the money and then they drove me onto the field a long way from the road. They told me to kneel down in front of a haystack and stood either side of me, each with a revolver in their hand. I said my prayer in the face of death for the ninth time, the *widdni*, the prayer of the dying and then they began to lay into me, head, back, sides everything in me was beaten to a pulp, but I still managed to hear the brutes say [«]he doesn't need a bullet any more. [«] What happened then I don't know. I fell unconscious ...

RICHARD ZACH

(1919–1943)

My Loved One

They have buried me behind cold grey walls,
suffocating the sighs and screams of hate at the same
time;
They have locked me up in chains and ropes that
bind,
My soul is gagged, my spirit suffering all
the torments devised by a scheming mind,
Though the bars, barriers and jailers separate me
from you,
cut off from everything; eternal exile announced,
but my faith burns,
My will is a witness.
Already blind and shaking, dazed from want,

and confused from waiting, embedded in scars,
Released to the endless, grinding hours;
I know they can never kill my striving,
no matter how many hangmen they call on,
I feel: they will never destroy my work
even as they condemn me shamelessly today,
I know: they can never rend us asunder
and every torment will just weld us together.
Was I ever closer to you?

In front of the blood court

I do not fear the death that grins from the masks,
the judgement you thoughtlessly pronounce
is not obscured by a fantasy sweet with incense .
I know the hangman already waits.
Bored, you fill the final forms,
Your hooked noses playing,
condescending, with the mouse.

What do still want to squeeze out of me you
                                        hypocratics?
You have me. So cool your wrath, poke
at all the wounds, Now don't forget it;
that's what your sort knows best.
But all your effort is in vain,
meanwhile you may stuff yourself again.

We want to entertain ourselves as well as possible.
»Now,« you say, »instead of begging for comfort?«

I won't cling to your shirttails.
It's obvious: nothing will be late.
That's why I want to be cheerful, exactly why.
You have to understand, I love each and every hour.

NIKOLAUS HARNONCOURT

(∗ 1929)

Wartime

I'm surprised to find that so much of the normal HJ[*]
service has remained in my memory. I keep seeing
myself in those offices along with thirty others, all
subjected to the ›Weltanschauung schooling,‹ or in
some brutal fight during manoeuvres around Graz.

Another course was called ›Pre-military Training.‹
The instructor was an SS man I saw again later with
repulsion when he was working as a stage hand in the
Graz opera. We were all put on top of a water tower
on the side of a hill and then they asked us, who dares
not to jump? I knew that in the previous class two
people had broken their arms when they leapt. I also
new that it needed more courage to say no than to
jump.

---

[*] HJ = Hitler Jugend = Hitler Youth. In 1936 Hitler outlawed all
other youth groups except for the HJ. As an important aspect of
the National Socialist (Nazi) program, the aim of the HJ was to
take full control over children's the social and political education.

So I raised my hand. I think I was the only one and then I had to step forward at evening roll call and let myself be screamed at – coward.

But those are only minor events. In the memories of that time fear plays a big role. Fear of people with party badges, fear of certain teachers or that something you had heard at home in passing would slip out ... and also the awareness that I myself would have to go to war in a very short time. Rene had had to go into the army already.

Nothing ever happened to us at the tower, though. When you are a child you don't get scared as easily. The older ones knew much more about what might happen, of course. I had to locate where clouds of smoke came from with a telescope and report it to the fire brigade.

Once, I was on my way to Hilm Pond on my bike and the bombs fell immediately after the alarm, perhaps just a hundred meters away. The pressure wave was so strong it knocked me off my bike. When I got the bomb's bearings, looking from the vantage point at Hilm, the smoke was coming from exactly where our house was. Then I was dreadfully afraid that everyone was dead. At the first opportunity I cycled down and saw that the Anatomical Institute of the University had been destroyed, five houses further on. It was also in Goethestrasse. My whole family and all the other inhabitants of the house sat trembling in the cellar. Every time there was a sound one of them kept repeating, our fighters, our fighters ...he was so afraid of the bombers and had convinced himself that they were our own fighters. It was dreadful to see how afraid those old civilians were.

Then I had to dig out the cellars of bombed houses. In the evenings after a day of excavating cellars we got a meal. Barley broth or something like that and cigarettes, ten pitiful cigarettes. Half of them I smoked myself, the other half I traded for bread. The digging out time lasted about fourteen days.

KLAUS HOFFER

(∗ 1942)

Amongst the stinging nettles in the rubbish

My father had been a high-level Nazi functionary in Graz. So after his death in the spring of 1944 my mother, along with other, temporarily fatherless Nazi families, fled from the bombing of the city to Upper Styria where we lived in a house on an estate of terraced dwellings built by Polish concentration camp prisoners. We were there till 1950.

Before our move back to Graz I was there twice. My parents former flat was now occupied by a ›communist‹ who had moved in with his parents, wife and child. I stood in the courtyard of the neighbouring house with my mother and looked up at the balcony that nowadays is part of my flat and at the small, cunning woman, the mother of the flat thief, as she hung washing out to dry. (Years later, late one evening in summer, she lost her dentures on a road in the Stifting Valley. We were on our way home from our grandparents and searched for them in the dark with aid of a torch until my sister found them. In the meantime we found out who we were helping.) During one of these two short stays (they served the purpose of winning back ›our‹ flat) my mother and I went along Nagler-gasse in order to visit friends. The left hand side had been totally destroyed by bombs. In Brandhofgasse, on the way there, between two houses was a gap: one was missing. Up on the level of second storey, as if it was a doll's house, there was a small piece of ceiling left over and on it was a toilet bowl, the cistern still up above it on the wall.

This toilet had something airy, stubborn about it.

Almost every Sunday all five of us marched the unvaried, hopeless way through Leechgasse and Schanzelgasse to our grandparents in Stifting. The refuse glittered from between the stinging nettles on the banks of the Kroisbach. In the bomb craters in Ries Wood, where we played as children, the nettles grew between pieces of broken glass and rubble. In my memory the forti-fied building that was the provincial hospital on our way home appeared outlandish, like a Tibetan palace high up in a steel-blue evening sky.

These are the earliest, permanent impressions of Graz: rubble, stinging nettles, war material, shards, the camouflage ochre of the hospital and dull Sunday afternoons with grandfather and grandmother who couldn't stand the sight of me. The gloomy flat in Goethestrasse, the gloomy flat in Leonhard where we brought up to be taroc players and sat either at the small, square, copper table to eat a snack or at the green-covered, round, dining-come-card table to play in a living room which had something of a Turkish salon, with its real carpets, semi-darkness and grandmother's cold cigarette smoke.

INGEBORG DAY

(* 1940)

Where are the Jews

(...) do you know what those Nazis have done? Concentration camps, here, right in the middle of Austria, why aren't there any Jews around any more, none in the school, none in Wetzelsdorf, none in Graz, are they all ... was every single one of them killed?

KARLHEINZ BÖHM

(∗ 1928)

In my father's city

I scarcely knew Graz at all. As a child I was only once
or twice in my father's hometown, a few days in all.
Being together with my parents had become something foreign to me, after many years of separation I
had to form a relationship with them again. I was still
a child when the war began when I had been sent with
my mother to Kufstein and, a year later, to boarding
school. Now I was seventeen and was suddenly supposed to live with my parents in very close proxim-
ity. Perhaps it was here, in my hometown, that I spent
the most difficult two years of my life.

Initially the three of us lived in one rented room. It
belonged to a distant cousin of my fathers in Graz. My
parents, who had been used to sleeping separately
their whole life, now had to share a bed with each
other. I lay on a mattress on the floor. A few weeks
later we got a three-and-a-half room flat in number 36
Kerblergasse. There was a bedroom for my mother, a
bedroom for my father, a sitting room and a small
kitchen. Behind the kitchen there was a pantry or
servant's room three and a half by one and a half meters. I lived in this tiny room with a small bed and a
table. Later it would be place where terrible events
happened.

Graz lay within the English zone of occupation. There was little to eat. The staple food was called polenta, an Italo-Austrian term for everything that you can make from maize or maize flour. We ate polenta for breakfast, dinner and tea; as bread, in cake as desert and even as a sandwich spread. There was almost no meat or vegetables. Even so, polenta is still one of my favourite dishes. Prepared in the Styrian way it is specially tasty. I love to order polenta whenever I am home for a visit.

Home is Styria? I'm going to have to explain that. In point of fact, immediately after the war, my father's natal city would become my legal city of birth. In 1946 or 1947 I got a right of domicile for the City of Graz, the »Natal City Roll,« as we call it. My father bequeathed it to me, as he did the Austrian citizenship. So, even though I was born a German and grew up in Germany, I became an Austrian like my father. At first my relationship to Austria was not very pronounced and my attitude to this country rather critical but in the course of time I became something like an »Austrian by training.« When I want to, I talk in a hotchpotch of Austrian dialects. However, it is only in recent years that I have been able to form a deeper relationship to my Austrian home country.

Back to 1946. At that time we got food coupons but we were a little better off than the others because my uncle, my father's brother, owned a sanatorium just across the road from our flat. As a doctor and the owner of sanatorium »Hansa,« he was better off than

140

most people. We also profited from that. You could only get food coupons when you could prove that you had seen certain films about Nazi atrocities. Films about concentration camps and, strangely enough, about venereal diseases. I remember them with horror. For example, one film was called »The Creeping Poison.« It showed male and female sexual organs which had been eaten away and the most horrible things in order to make people use condoms. Not having had sexual intercourse, this film was a shock for me. I got an even greater shock from the concentration camp film, a joint production by the Americans and the Russians who had filmed the half starving survivors at the end of the war. They were horrifying pictures that were crucial in increasing my hate and abhorrence of National Socialism.

I should have had another two years at the »Lyceum Alpinum« before I took my matura.* That meant I had to be put in school again in Graz. In Austria the school system which had existed prior to 1938 was reintroduced with a few small changes. There were subjects such a philosophy and ethics which had not existed in Switzerland. My parents registered me in the Kepler Gymnasium as an external student for the matura exams and sent me for private tutoring to a preparatory school for the matura. In a one-and-a-half year crash course I tried to adapt to the Austrian school system and catch up on the work of the previ-

---

* Final school examinations taken around the age of 18 and a prerequisite for university studies.

ous two years before the matura. I was lucky to get a funny teacher – a small, hunchbacked, asthmatic man. Out of all the teachers from my time at school I liked him best, really.

During this period my father was fully involved with his denazification proceedings. As with other artists and high profile conductors such as Wilhelm Furt-wängler, Herbert von Karajan and Clemens Krauss, my father was prohibited from performing after the war because of his alleged identification with Nazi Germany. He was repeatedly accused of not having emigrated like the two great conductors Bruno Walter and Otto Klemperer, two persecuted Jewish musi-cians, who continued their careers abroad. By the way my father did try to get out of the country near the end of the war. In summer 1944 at the Zurich Festival his Swiss friends Wilhelm Backhaus, Dr. Willi Schuh and an old school friend called Gustav Hussnigg who was living in Lugano offered to pay his living ex-penses if he wanted to stay in Switzerland. In his au-tobiography my father writes:

»As I tentatively inquired in Vienna about a stay in Switzerland I got the garnished reply ›You have your old mother and two brothers in Graz, we can hold on to them.‹ Right away I knew that ›sippenhaftung‹[*] would come into effect and I couldn't square it with my conscience to leave mother and brothers to the mercies of the Nazis. It was the 2nd of August. Shortly

---

[*] Where all members of a family are punished for the ›wrongdo-ings‹ of one member.

afterwards the theatre was closed and total war declared by Goebbels in his ›marvellously‹ staged speech in the Palace of Sport in Berlin. Nevertheless in Vienna I did everything to prevent my personnel being called up to the army or drafted into the armament industry.«

It was absurd to suspect my father of being a Nazi even if he might have aroused the impression that he was an opportunist. In the last chapter I recounted his upper-middle class origins and his being brought up with a certain attitude to obeying authority. His apolitical conduct can be explained by this upbringing and his attempt to save himself by immersing himself in his art. He was never a member of the Nazi party. In his autobiography he tells of how, in 1932, a Hamburg lawyer attempted to recruit him for the NSDAP. My father let him stew a little and then, to his surprise, said »I belong to only *one* party: the musical party.«

My father was always steadfastly anti-war and anti-militarist as was his father before him. He passed that on to me. I have to thank him for the fact that I am a fundamental and resolute opponent of everything military. I have never been in the army myself and have never worn a uniform – in contrast to my father. When the First World War broke out in 1914 he was called up because he was a completely healthy young man. Along with his horse Nepomuk he went to the so-called Train division that had to provide for further supplies in Graz. How he managed to avoid service

in the field was something he liked to recount often
– a story I always found funny:

»I was soon made a corporal, then platoon sergeant.
As such I had to check the stable sentries. In the
Train division we had draughthorses in addition to the
officer's horses. One night around twelve I went to the
stable. The sentry was totally drunk and I had to bawl
at him according to regulations: ›You drunken chap
…‹ as is usual in the army. A Pinzgauer horse woke
up because of this and kicked out. It caught me and
I fell down unconscious, only to wake up again in my
bed in Schulgasse 17. The doctor diagnosed a heavy
haematoma and a bruised bladder which was not
without its dangers. I lay there with an ice-bag and
the whole time I got better and better I thought: ›It
would be a shame to die a hero's death and how can
I loaf around after I'm back on my feet. In other words,
what's the best way to escape from the army?‹

My regimental doctor was an angel, a private doctor,
Dr. Mitterer …Due to my accident I got a C-clearance
– only suitable for service on home the home front. I
could only be posted in a serious crisis and so had to
do duty in the office.

The war situation got more and more difficult. I got
bronchitis and the doctor who was a close friend and
for whom I always played the piano, wrote a diagno-
sis for me –suspicion of TB. It was, of course, a completely exaggerated medical certificate. They even
asked me ›Do you want to claim compensation?‹ That
was because you could get compensation for any harm

144

suffered while in the army. Of course I renounced my rights and with the medical certificate as completely unfit for service I then left the army without compensation. That was in 1916.

It would take another two years for my father's denazification proceedings to finally be concluded and for him to be authorised to perform as a conductor again. This extremely hard-working man suffered unbelievably from the work prohibition. He was at home a lot or together with both his brothers. I remember it as if it was just yesterday. Family life was, of course, very tense. We had to live from what my mother earned. She gave singing lessons and it was at that time that she discovered her marvellous voice and thus rediscovered the profession she had given up for my father. Incidentally, the piano came, like most of the rest of the furniture from Vienna. My parents had put it in storage when they left their house in 1945.

At home, when my mother was teaching, you had to be very quiet again. When she was not giving a class, my father sat in front of his scores. He read scores, worked on scores, learned scores by heart – incessantly, really. Again, you couldn't disturb him.

However, in any case I wasn't at home a lot because I had to swot up an enormous amount. Every day I sat in the matura school seven or eight hours, so I didn't have time for much else. Sometimes I played a little tennis and I had my first harmless flirtations.

I was also a late developer, as far as my relationship to women was concerned. I only had my first physical contact with a woman after we moved to Vienna in 1948. I was twenty then and the woman was the same age. She had a terrible past. Just like the girl in the waiting room in Salzburg station, this girl and her mother had been raped by the Russians. Incidentally, we still meet sometimes, even today. My first love in Graz was called, of all things, Sissi. A platonic love, by the way. I called my first daughter Sissi after her and not, as they tried to pin on me afterwards, because of the successful »Sissi« films ...

ALFRED KOLLERITSCH

(* 1931)

We are who we are

When I returned to the city after the end of the war, I entered *the* city I had left behind. The catch-word »construction« concealed that above all reconstruction was meant. The rubble was removed, the ruins began to grow over. I might have said the Graz had stayed Graz and at the time I felt grateful for it. Perhaps the people struck me as being more modest, the reconstruction seemed to give them less enjoyment than the fantasies of the preceding destruction. One lived with a skin that had been saved. The sale of things for the commanders of the Anschluss years turned into a grab it all of possessions that allowed one to forget the loss. Where previously the great word »orderly« ruled, now it was ›silence,‹ but not a despairing silence; more a keeping quiet. We learned that important people from before were dead, had fled or had been arrested. Some people regretted that, it left others cold. In general you didn't pay much attention to it. Revenge was usually taken for personal motives. In principle little happened, the new politicians tried hard to win over those who had been cleared. However, what should have happened within the totality (yes, the entire world even) that had, in this respect, become the world? I admit that I think with terror of the vengeful figures who first appeared as judges. They hit back with *their* truth, nothing more. The desire for the physical destruction of those who wantonly took life belonged to the same wandering and around and murdering all over the world. Even when the majority were still almost unaware of was National Socialism was (also those who had strongly supported it), democracy was adopted. The exception was, of course, those who were already painfully and doubtingly aware of a democratic tradition. However, it was precisely this tradition that was still treated with suspicion by the majority. The city's bourgeoisie (in the widest sense) remained nationalist, conservative, reactionary, just as they always had been. It remained cut off and committed to meanings *in* which it lived according to the guiding principle of the unchanged conception of itself, according to the customary masquerade: life goes on, nothing can shake us, the level of attained security is the whole truth. We are who we are. Graz is Graz. (…)

In the school I attended again after the war some of the teachers who taught were different. What we found out first was that because of the end of the war and the attendant long holiday we had forgotten the basics necessary for the upper classes. We did not talk about »past« subjects. We were spared the words of the Führer but otherwise everything remained as it had been. Our eyes were not opened to how things had been. To exaggerate a little, there was talk of the danger of communism but nothing said about resistance fighters. The homecoming of soldiers from captivity was not used as an occasion for reflection, the soldiers' homecoming was celebrated as a kind of perverse victory. We learned nothing of pain and only a little about hunger. During the war we had been told about the ›new man.‹ Those who had believed in that or spoken in favour of it were still the same people who, having dropped out of National Socialism, began to trot out democracy, still exercising their petty ways of power. Whatever was said loud and clear and in public against the past appeared to be said on the instructions of the occupying powers because Austria was still not free. I don't mean to imply that a mass re-education or a purgative brainwashing should have taken place. Who would have had the right to do it? The citizens of the period 1938 to 1945 would have had to take that step of renouncing it themselves, especially in the ›Stadt der Volkserhebung.‹ * That this didn't take place can only be explained by the fact the

---

* City of the People's Uprising

National Socialism in Graz was more than a passing cloud which had cast its shadow over the unsuspecting. They stretched out their arms to grasp it (or unleashed it themselves). The call came from a long tradition (as they say around here) – from an aspect that existed prior to the dialectic which is supposed to be part of the enlightenment. This aspect of a Grazer's humanity still lies too deep and undifferentiated in a ›nature‹ that rejects the term. To this day natural means nationalist, rooted in the soil, the inner being is still, as it always was, »in German hands« – or what ›German‹ is taken to mean since very little of German intellect and philosophic depth was ever felt here. Those pieces which were blasted out sank or dissolved into the whole, for example the ideas of the nationalists. Much of it takes place in the psyche of the Grazer, in his daily way of life. The little monads live alongside each other in isolation and maintain that living alongside each other is a social life ...

AENEAS SILVIUS PICCOLOMINI

(1405–1464)

Two Letters

Letter to Dionys Szech, Archbischop of Gran

Graz, 16th September, 1443

I write to you, Reverend Father, of what I recently saw in Styria. It is not true, so I submit to any judgment, even that of a Pole. And take the punishment meted out to those who bear false witness. In Styria there is a river which comes from the Alps and leads into the Drau which in turn flows into the Save. The Styrians call this river the Mur. On its bank lies a city which is called by its inhabitants Grecz. There an enormous mountain rises up from the plain, the sides of which fall away sheer. On the top there is a castle which, because of the nature of the place and human artifice, is very fortified and worth its kingly splendour. Gathered here are Austria's hopes, Hungary's yearning and Bohemia's worries, the youthful king Ladislaus, whom I saw at the royal court at the beginning of September together with his cousin, Emperor Friedrich and a great number of barons.

Letter to his Father

Graz, 20th September, 1443

Enea Silvio, poet, greets his father warmly!

Dear Father, You wrote that you didn't know whether
you should be happy or angry that God has granted
me offspring. From my point of view it is an occasion
to be celebrated and not one of sadness. What in this
world is sweeter than to reproduce your own image
whilst at the same time to proliferate one's blood and
to have someone to leave behind in the world? And
what is more blessed in this world than to see the
children of your children? I am very happy that my
seed brought forth fruit, that at my death something
from me will remain and I thank God that he formed
a little son for me in the womb of a woman, that a little Enea will play at home with you and mother and
give his grandparents all the pleasure that his father
would have given to them. Father, if you were happy
when I was born why not about the birth of my son?
Will his little countenance not delight you, when you
discover my features therein? Won't you like it when
the little scallywag hangs around your neck stokes
you in his childlike way? But you say at the end that
my violation causes you pain because I engendered
my son in a sinful relation? I don't know what you
think of me. You don't have a son that's made of stone
or iron since you yourself are made of flesh and blood.
You know what kind of a cock of the walk you used
to be and I'm no different. I belong neither to those
who are made of ice nor to the hypocrites who would
rather appear to be irreproachable than actually be

so. I admit my mistake openly because I'm not holier than David and not wiser than Salomon. Because my mistake has happened often, and I know no-one who has not done it ...

GALILEO GALILEI

(1564–1642)

Letter to Johannes Kepler in Graz

I received your book, learned sir, which you sent me through Paulus Amberger not a few days ago but rather only a few hours ago. Since the same Paulus announced his own return to Germany I would regard it as ungrateful if I did not express my thanks to you in the present letter. Let me thank you then, especially for the evidence of your friendship with which you dignify me. Up till now I know your work only from the introduction but I have understood your intention to some extent and really wish for myself the special luck of having a man such as this who is a friend of truth and my companion in the search for it. It is unfortunate that people who strive for truth and do not follow a form of mistaken philosophy are so rare. But here is not the place to complain of the ailments of the our century but to be happy along with you about such beautiful ideas being proof of the truth. So I would add only this, and promise that I will read your book carefully because I am certain I will find the most wonderful things in it. And I will be happy do this all the more because I came to share Copernicus' views many years ago and from this position discovered the causes of many natural processes which would not have been explicable on the basis of common understanding. I have written much on direct and indirect proofs but have not yet dared to publish it, intimidated by the fate of Copernicus himself, our teacher. He has won undying fame amongst the few and is laughed and whistled at by infinitely more (because the number of fools is so great). In fact, I would risk making my thoughts public if there were more people of your convictions but since that is not the case I will refrain. The pressure of time and the urgent desire to read your book compel me to close by assuring you of my affection, I am at your service, do not fail to send me pleasant news of yourself.

Padua, 4th August, 1597
Your companion in friendship
Galilaeus Galilaeus
Mathematician at the Academy of Padua

JOHANNES KEPLER

(1571–1630)

Letter to Galileo in Parma

In each place there is only one mathematician and where that is the case it is for the best. If he then had a like-minded contemporary he should demand a letter from him so that by showing the letter (yours was also useful in this manner) he will be able to create the impression amongst the learned that agreement reigns in the circles of the professors of mathematics. But why would you need such cunning? Be of good courage Galileo and step forward. If I am correct in my assumptions, there are few among the European mathematicians who would differ from us. Such is the power of truth. If Italy appears to you to be unsuitable for publication and you have to expect obstacles, it may be that Germany would grant us that freedom. But enough of that. Please let me know what you have discovered that would be favourable to Copernicus, privately at least if you do not wish to do so publicly.

Now I would like to ask you for an observation, since I do not own any instruments I must resort to others. Do you have a quadrant on which minutes and quarter minutes can be read? If so, observed during the 19th December the maximum and minimum height of the middle star in the tail of the Great Bear in the same night. Similarly observed on the 26th December both heights for the Polar Star. Already observed the height of first star on the 19th March 89, 12 o'clock at night, the second on the 28th September also at 12 o'clock. If there is a difference between the two observations, as I would like there to be, from one or more minutes or even 10 to 15, it would be evidence for something that would have great consequences for the whole of astronomy. If, however, there is simply no difference at least we will collectively harvest the fame of some highly important problems which have not been tested by anyone [fixed star parallax]. Enough for those with understanding! I am sending you 2 more copies [of Prodromus] because Amberger told me that you wanted some more. Those to whom you send the book should pay for it with a written remark about it. Farewell and answer me with a long letter.

Graz, 13th October 1597

Your dear friend
Master Johannes Kepler

FRANZ SCHUBERT

(1797–1828)

A Letter to Graz, 1827

I have already found out that I felt very good when I was in Graz and I can't really get Vienna into my head, of course it's a little large but lacking in warmth, openness, real thoughts and reasonable words and in particular in witty deeds. You don't really know if you're clever or stupid because there is so much is babbled conversation and it is seldom, if ever, that you attain a heartfelt gaiety. Of course it's possible that I am to blame with the way I am, warming to others but slowly. In Graz I very soon learned the natural and open way of being with and next to each other, something which would certainly have gone deeper with a longer stay. In particular I will never forget the friendly inn, the lovely landlady, the vigorous Pachleros and the little Faust where I spent the most enjoyable days in a long time. In the hope of being able to express my thanks in an appropriate way,

With the greatest respect,
I remain your faithful servant,
Franz Schubert

P. S. I hope to be able to send you the opera book in the next few days.

JOHANN NEPOMUK NESTROY

(1801–1862)

Letter to Ernst Stainhauser

Graz, May 2nd, 1861

Stainhauser, My Dear Friend
...Man does not live from just reading newspapers but also, and mainly, from food. For that, however, you need an appetite. If you have devoted an hour to studying the newspapers, then you need at least a two hour walk in order to revive the appetite that, as a legitimate patriot, you must have lost by reading. Can you be hungry for beef when you think that those oxen are coming from Poland and Hungary and that as a consequence even they will become infected a little by the epidemic (called the ›nationality swindle‹ by the political doctors) presently grazing there. Can you appreciate pork when you consider that swine breeding is specially strong in Hungary? Doesn't the bite

of lamb in your mouth turn bad when you think of the lamb-like meekness shown in Pesth about the Emperor's eagle standard being torn down and that this outrage was only found unacceptable in Croatia? If you may not maltreat the eagle with insouciance in Croatia why can you do so in Hungary? Are they not the same eagle? I'll have to ask a hunter about that. With the desserts you have the same irritation. How can you enjoy the Bavarian dalken* when you think that the inedible Rieger and Palacky are also part of it? Can you get a Tyroler strudel down while thinking about the Innsbrucker Landtag and all that revolting stuff with which a few intolerant Oroviste and like-minded state haemorrhoids dare to besmirch the Emperor's liberal law giving confessional equality? I can assure you that an appetite-producing walk has become the absolute necessity of life sine qua non. So we often promenade of a morning in the Leonhard Woods which are less than twenty minutes away and there, looking towards Gleisdorf (eastwards), I always remember that from Gratz to Fürstenfeld is a good two miles further than Vienna to Marchegg. So in Gratz we are a good two miles further away from Hungary than we would be in Vienna. Gratz is really wonderfully situated! I often visit Schlossberg and – something that doesn't require more than tuppence worth of fantasy – when looking at the clouds piling up, make a jump from the atmospheric to the political as they billow almost announcing a storm. There are many who

---

* A type of fritter made from a yeast dough

would like to call our situation hopeless, but even those of little courage cannot claim that it is not to be helped since we still have the Reichsrat[*]. And even if the difficulties were ten time what they are, I rely on Grillparzer …

Your idle friend

J. Nestroy

LUDWIG BOLTZMANN

(1844–1906)

Letter to Hermann von Helmholtz in Berlin
(confirmatory evidence of Maxwell's theory)

1872 XI 1 Graz

Greatly Esteemed Privy Councillor

(…) I have continued with my investigations here in Graz. I wanted to find the answer to the question whether a change in the capacity of condensers by inserting layers of various materials really results in the electrification of the smallest particle of that material or whether that simply results from the fact that the electricity works its way through the material in a different way to air. In the first case, previously unelectrified balls of sulphur, hard rubber etc. would have to be attracted to an electrically charged body

---

[*] Imperial Diet

without being electrified by means of a cable, that is, simply as a result of the dielectric polarisation of the smallest particle in the same way as only the smallest particles of a piece of soft iron are polarised by a magnet. In contrast, in the second case there would be no reason for such an attraction to be present. This attraction did in fact take place and had almost the predicted intensity. I calculated it from the dielectric constants using very similar formulas to those derived from the magnetisation constants used to calculate the attraction of soft iron. There is something else I can't get round telling you. Up till now, I was always of the opinion (and I think you also voiced the same opinion when I was still in Berlin) that according to Maxwell's theory light and electricity are identical and that my dielectric constants must be the same as the refraction quotients. As I was tabulating all the values of the dielectric constants, I was distressed that they diverged so much from the quotients of refraction while at the same time I noticed that they were always approximately the square of the quotient of refraction. Like a bolt from the blue I had a thought – was it possible that Maxwell's theory proposes precisely that because the rate of reproduction is always proportional to the square root of the forces. I looked up Maxwell's treatise and there is was clearly stated – the dielectric constants must be proportional to the square of the refractive exponents. The magnetic induction constant being near to one for all of these materials. Thus I have to consider that my experiments are confirmation of Maxwell's theory! (...)

Graz in Styria, Heinrichstr. Nr.3, Ground Floor, right.

HUGO WOLF

(1860–1903)

Two Letter to Graz
(To Heinrich Potpeschnigg, a friend and pianist in Graz who was also a patron)

Döbling, 12th January 1892

My Dear Doctor,
The good people of Graz appear to be in no hurry to get to know me from my reproductive side. –

Well, I can wait. Once I have the best singers of the world working under me and also, perhaps, a philharmonic orchestra, and if I distribute free tickets and a free snack I'll probably be able to find an open ear in the Grazer public, don't you think? Oh, the Philistines!

Well, I won't condemn this artistic Sodom out of hand, as long as there is one just man in it whose hand I can shake in friendship, as your devoted friend does now,

Hugo Wolf

Döbling, 16th May, 1892

My Dear Doctor,
It was with great pleasure and not a little satisfaction that I gathered from the Grazer Tagblatt, which happenstance placed in my hands, the news of a concert of your Wagner Society which had placed its powers exclusively at the service of my work and announced the concert simply as a »Hugo Wolf« Evening. This

was a feat that could certainly not have been expected of my local academic Wagner Society since the »leading figures« of this association have long ago forgotten how concern themselves with »small things.« Such »mediocre entertainment« is best left to people of the provinces who can then see if they like it. That my fellow Styrians like it so much, warms my heart. The enjoyment cannot have been as »mediocre« as my »patrons« here would like to believe and if you can believe the reports in the newspaper, the success was something approaching the sensational. Bravo! And again bravo! Bravissimo! The Grazer Wagner Society did it well and proved without a doubt that not only »Nürnbergers« can do things. Long live he who lives and let's live! Long live the life-giving, life-affirming Wagner Society in Graz. Ad infinitum …

I have just received from an old woman friend of mine from the Hotel Semmering a review of the concert in the Tagespost. Now I am more or less informed as to the way the programme was constituted I can only say that I find it praiseworthy, contrary to your fears. All the same I would ask that you send a copy of the programme as soon as possible – better send a few copies – in order that I can admire your strategic talent from the beginning. I certainly hope to be able to make use of your friendly invitation this summer at the time you proposed.

Hugo Wolf

SIGMUND FREUD

(1856–1939)

A postcard to Martha Freud from Graz

28th August, 1904

Day was as expected, after a pleasant journey I'm
again lodged with the good solid animal* in order to
fill the gaps in my diet. The beginning was splendid,
the pilsner is very good. At 11.30!! continuing to
Trieste.

ROBERT MUSIL

(1880–1942)

Two letters to the philosopher
Alexius Meinong in Graz

Brünn, December 30th, 1908

Your Honour, esteemed Professor,
My cousin, Dr. Schuch has informed me that your
honour has shown a positive interest in assigning the
post of assistant in Graz to myself. Since I am at
present engaged in correspondence with the Techni-

---

* Grand Hotel Elephant, Südtirolerplatz.

cal College in Munich with regard to habilitation[*] there under very favourable conditions I would request your honour to grant me a few days before I give you my answer.

With the assurance that I would consider it a great gain to work under your direction in Graz should circumstances so allow and with my sincere thanks for offering me the opportunity I remain

Your humble servant
Dr. Robert Musil

January 18th, 1909
Berlin, W50. Regensburgerstrasse 15

Your Honour, esteemed Professor,
Please excuse for withholding my answer for so long. The reason lay in the difficulty of the decision. In the end the affair in Munich turned out to be completely different to what it was in the beginning and what was promised but I still cannot decide whether to go to Graz. I would like to ask you, most esteemed professor, to believe me when I say that I would not only have regarded it as a great honour but also as the most considerable gain I could imagine for my scientific further education to be able to work alongside you. My love of literature is not less than my love of science and because of it the apparently easy decision became a critical matter for me.

In judging the relevant circumstances as they appear to me today, I believe that I have to resist the

---

[*] qualification as a university level lecturer.

temptation to go the Graz. I am most conscious of the fact that this judgement is not fully comprehensible nor is it definitive. It might well be that I would want to undo it in the near future but I am afraid of answering your kindness with delay any longer and feel it is my duty to give you an honest reply.

In asking you to remember me favourably in the future despite the fact that I have not been able to show my gratitude for it at this time, I remain your obedient servant,

Dr. Robert Musil

ANTON WILDGANS

(1881–1932)

Letter to his wife

10. 10. 1924

»Today I walked from Rosenberg over the »High Plain« to Maria Trost. It was a glorious autumn day, cool and at the same time warm because of the sun. This region is unique in its beauty. I can only compare it to the area around Naples. Spanish chestnuts grow in gardens and woods all around and a secondary summer flora covers the lower lying and lush meadows. Only a few of the trees are already clothed in their autumn colours, everything else is still summery green.«

RAOUL HAUSMANN

(1886–1971)

A Letter

20th December 66

My dear friend Kolleritsch,
Why do I think a lot of you? Because you are a man
with convictions, and what's more important, you act
according to them. You will understand better what
I am saying when I tell you that most publishers reject my manuscripts with contempt, especially in
Germany. With the French texts things are a little
better but most magazines have no money and so almost nothing appears.

In March there should be a special issue with my
work in the magazine »Phantomas,« 50 pages of unpublished texts but the man has no money at the moment. That he is very enthusiastic about my writing
changes nothing.

But the Streit – Zeit – Schrift* had already accepted
a piece from me and used it in their brochure. Then
they would only send me a copy if I paid DM 4.- and
when I got it my text wasn't in it.

And after all that why I shouldn't be delighted with
you?

I have already made contact with Frau Arp and I
will select unpublished writings by Arp with her but

---

* Literally: Streit = dispute; Zeit = time; Schrift = Writing; Zeitschrift = periodical, magazine and all the other combinations.

please write to me before that and tell me how many pages you can publish.

An Arp volume with 627 pages has just been published by Gallimard and a catalogue to an exhibition in Sankt Gallen, both of which contain excellent things, German and French.

Naturally we will get only unpublished material for »manuskripte.«

What I wrote about Friederike Mayröcker's book you can maybe stick in the book discussions section.

Now to my trip to Graz: for the moment this is impossible because I have very great difficulties with customs.

Hannah Höch returned part of my Dada work to me (after 44 years) but now the customs authorities have got wind of it and I may have to pay FF1.000.- for »first time importation into France« so that I can get possession of my property. In addition there is also a very unpleasant matter with the Museum of the 20th Century in Vienna whose director has illegally appropriated a number of my works and will not turn them over to me.

So, on one hand there are weeks of trouble and on the other my eyes which are so bad that I cannot travel alone. But how about you coming to me here in Limoges?

You would be able to see an enormous number of things that I couldn't have taken to Graz.

I intended to give you a lithograph for Christmas, one from the 300 numbered prints I made for the Dada Tresor for the Simmen Publishing House in

Zurich but I'll send it in the new year because till after Christmas we have nothing but continuous postal and railway strikes. I don't even know if you'll get this letter.

In the meantime I wish you and your wife best wishes for the new year,

Raoul Hausmann

ERNST DECSEY

(1870–1941)

Schubert

The relationship is of long standing, beginning during the master's youth. Schubert associated with Graz artists early on but he only set foot in the city a year before he died. One of his oldest friends was our Anselm Hüttenbrenner who was born in Graz in 1794 and died in the friendly, neighbouring Ober-Andritz in 1868. Hüttenbrenner went to Vienna to study composition under the famous Salieri. In 1815 as a twenty-one year old he was introduced to Schubert who was then eighteen. Though often interrupted, this interchange continued until Schubert's death. They were close friends and Schubert, who called Anselm his »coffee, wine and punch brother,« often wrote the most wonderful things in his little parlour. Thus it was that on the 21st of February at twelve midnight he

composed the delightful and famous »Forelle[*]« in
Hüttenbrenner's flat in Neubad. Schubert was also on
a friendly footing with Anselm's brothers – with Heinrich,
who went on to be a university professor in Graz and
with Josef Hüttenbrenner one of the oldest and most
uncompromising Schubert enthusiasts. Schubert is
said to have been annoyed by him and remarked, »he
likes everything I do!« Johann Baptiste Jenger (1792
–1856) was one of the first Schubertians. He was a
military official and a superb pianist on the side and
was befriended with Schubert before he was officially
posted to Graz in 1819. He remained in Graz until
1825 and worked as the secretary in the service of the
young Styrian Music Society in whose concerts he
often appeared as a soloist. It was also Jenger who, in
1823, proposed and carried through the motion to
make Schubert an honorary member of the Music
Society on the basis »that this composer, although
still young, has given evidence in his compositions
that he will occupy a high position as a composer at
some time.« The appointment was communicated to
Schubert in the form of a diploma which, in order to
save costs, was given to Anselm Hüttenbrenner who
was to give it to Josef Hüttenbrenner in Vienna who
in turn made sure that it got into Schubert's hands.
Beethoven, who had also been made honorary member the year before, had not replied but Schubert expressed his thanks in a letter of the 20th September
1823 in which he remarked, amongst other things,
that he »would be so free as to present the honourable

---

[*] Trout

society with a symphonic score as early as possible.« And so it came to pass. Schubert sent the more than glorious B minor symphony composed in 1822. He gave it to Anselm via Josef Hüttenbrenner. It may be that Anselm forgot the score or that other factors played a role, but during the time he was director of the Music Society he never performed one of Schubert's works. In short, the wonderful symphonic fragment was lost for a long time until Johann Herbeck, the Viennese royal musical director coincidentally paid Anselm a visit in 1865 which led to its premier. More details about this are reported by Dr. F. Bischoff in this chronicle of the Music Society and Ludwig Herbeck in his father's biography. The fact of the matter is that this delightful work, lost and luckily re-found, is the one which Schubert would have intended for the Styrian Music Society if he had managed to write a dedication on the copy.

Schubert began an intellectual relationship with the Styrian poet Gottfried Ritter von Leitner (1800–1890) also in the year 1823. He composed the wonderful song »Drang in die Ferne« to the latter's verse at that time but he only met the poet personally when he visited Graz in 1827.

The master left Vienna with Jenger as autumn drew near, as our countryman Richard Heuberger tells us in his Schubert biography. The Pachler family, who were also acquainted with Beethoven, had repeatedly extended an invitation to him to visit the beautiful city on the Mur and Schubert, who admired Frau Leopoldine Pachler, an artist highly thought of by Beethoven, would have accepted it long before were it not for the fact that he had to wait for one of his intermittent sources of money to materialise. When this happily came to pass, Schubert was treated to some highly stimulating and pleasant days in the charming »Hallerschlossl« on the Ruckerl mountains where the Pachlers lived and from which there was a wonderful panoramic view of the mountains and city. And there he found what most musicians enjoy, »wine, women and song.« Schubert met his friend Anselm Hüttenbrenner here. He had nicknamed »Schilcherl«[*] while Schubert himself was given the name »Schwammerl.[**]« With the encouragement of Frau Pachler the master wrote the music here to Leitner's »The Lance Bearer from Wallenstein,« »Crusade« and »The Fisherman's Luck in Love,«[***] after having composed pieces for many other Leitner poems. Of the things which owe their origin to the visit to Graz, only »Gräzer Salopp,« and »Grätzer Waltzer« will be mentioned. Schubert, who visited the theatre here as well, appears to have tried to put on his opera »Alfonso and Estrella« in Graz. However, after two orchestra rehearsals it was put to one side as being »far too difficult.«

---

[*] Lit. A local wine

[**] Lit. little mushroom

[***] The original German titles are as follows: »Wallensteiner Lanzknecht,« »Kreuzzug,« and »Fischer's Liebesglück.«

LEOPOLD RITTER VON SACHER-MASOCH

(1836–1895)

The »Schwarzen Punkte« and their Opponents

After I has spent yet another month in the beautiful
metropolis on the blue Danube, I have to admit that
that great village called Graz made a quite amusing
impression. I am really amazed at the streets, the
people and the prevailing conditions. If, like an inhabitant of Gotham, you never leave Graz, or have at
most have undertaken a journey to Puntigam and
Judendorf, you may quote a variation of Goethe's
verse from the Roman Elegies all the same – »Oh,
Graz, you are a world!« If you have chosen to bind
yourself to the soil of Graz for even a few years you
might be able retain the illusion that you live in a
large city. However, as soon as you have spent some
time in the real wide world and then return to Graz,
it is almost a shock how small everything is. Graz is
spread out but it appears that this is only so that
alongside 10,000 intelligent people, 80,000 Abderites[*]
can find space. In every other respect it is as small
as the capital of Lilliput in which any half-way developed person is regarded as a giant striking terrible
fear into little hearts and minds ...

---

[*] An inhabitant of Abdera, in Thrace, regarded as the fools of classical antiquity.

... My dear Dr. Svoboda, as with many other terms, you appeared to be very unclear of the meaning with regard to scandal as well. It leaves me with no other choice but to teach you once and for all what can be understood under misuse of the press. It is a scandal when public opinion is led astray by falsehoods and fraudulent promises. It is a scandal when facts are falsified. It is a scandal when unimportant people are aggrandized to greatness and reputable, experienced men are diminished and you have the audacity to throw dirt by slandering them.

It is a scandal when talent is suppressed and mediocrity encouraged as a matter of principle. Misuse of the press also includes dragging the private lives of respectable people who are in no way part of public life wilfully and maliciously through the dirt just in order to gain some benefit and, in so doing to, destroy the peace of honourable families. However, when people push themselves forward, play a role in public life and in that role act meanly, egotistically or incompetently such that the interests of all are placed in danger or suffer damage, and this is exposed by the use of a lamp of Diogenes wielded with honest intent and unusual courage in the service of truth and justice then, Dr. Svoboda, this is only a scandal and misuse of the press in the eyes of those who have reason to tremble at the thought that one of these days the paper cloak of honour covering their vanity will be ripped away.

It is nothing new that men of darkness feel pain in their eyes from light of truth and find that scandalous.

172

There is a resolution of the Council of Frankfurt from the year 1779 which describes Lessing's »Nathan« as a »suspicious book« with »scandalous content.« What Lessing had to bear from the honourable councillors of Frankfurt I can only be regarded as a compliment when it pertains to a person like Svoboda and the Grazer »Tagespost« that organ of political scandal and aesthetic senselessness.

The intellectuals of Graz will only thank me when I reinstate the truth which has been systematically concealed and denied its place of honour in Abdera on the Mur. With this spiritually independent section of the inhabitants, the »Tagespost« lost all credibility long ago. This was proved in Svoboda's case by the almost devastating personal defeat he has suffered because of the election of Rechbauer.

There are credulous, lazy-thinking, good souls in the public who expressed their pain by way of a advertisement in the »Tagespost« and who have accused me of attacking a generally respected figures in the »Schwarzen Punkten.« If this was to be accepted as a serious point of disputation it would be like shooting at sitting ducks.

Considered more carefully, who are these generally respected figures that I attacked? Two young women whom respectable people have slandered in the most ungrateful and malicious way in the world – a profiteer known throughout the city who has the happiness of more than one family and more than one life on her conscience – and a theatre director who has reduced the Grazer Theatre to the same level as that of Znaim or Ödenburg and who once sold his principles for 30 florins a month and a winter coat.

If these are generally respected people in Graz, then I would prefer general contempt for myself.

It is not my nature to fight my battles with the help of the authorities or with any outside help at all which is why I preferred to stop publishing the »Schwarzen Punkte« in the »Grazer Morgenpost.« I did not want to bring the editor of this journal whom I personally love and value into conflict either with the good souls in the public nor with higher authorities. The »Morgenpost« would then be a very respectable pistol for me, but one that didn't fire. Instead I have acquired a pistol of my own. It only fires once a month but then properly.

A revolver may fire more often, but in the hand of a bad shot it would not bring me the slightest respect ...

ROBERT STOLZ

(1880–1975)

From the Radetzky March to Brahms

Birth

It was on a warm summer day in Graz, where I was born, that I heard Viennese music for the first time. Unfortunately at that moment I was occupied with other things and unable to abandon myself to the inspiring rhythms of the Radetzky March as it came through the open window of my mother's bedroom on that 25th of August 1880.

Outside a military band marched past. During that time I screamed my lungs out, upside down and with a bright red face. You have certainly guessed: I had just been born. The midwife had inspected me carefully to find out if I had all the necessary members and had just announced ceremoniously »It's a boy.« At exactly that moment the band had struck up. That was really just a coincidence, but looking back on it I've always taken it to be a bad omen.

»Grandfather« Brahms on his knees

The music world of his time always regarded Johannes Brahms as a brilliant artist but also as a rather arrogant, strange bird; as a snarling lone-wolf who despised most of the work of his contemporaries. He left no musical heirs behind so his compositional style died with him.

Musical history has accepted this harsh verdict and perhaps it is not completely erroneous – who can say? However, for his small circle of friends, to which my family also belonged, this musical titan was a quite different person – he was warm-hearted and generous and his self irony bordered on humility.

»What a shame that Johannes never married,« I heard my mother say once to my father.

»Johannes and marriage?« No woman in the world could live with him and certainly not if she was married to him, it would be her ruination. Apart from that he has been a bachelor far too long. He has brought order into his life and feels good as it is. The only woman who would ever have been able to tie him to her was Clara Schumann and she was wise enough to refrain from it!«

Father was not to be moved from his opinion and for good reasons because by no stretch of the imagination could it be said that Brahms visited us solely for the enjoyment of the beautiful Styrian landscape or even mother's good cooking and father's musical conversation. He was in love with a certain Miss von Gasteiger, one of our neighbours in Graz. Nevertheless mother had hit the nail on the head. If ever there had been an ideal grandfather it was Johannes Brahms. That is how I remember him.

He was wonderful with children. Not so long ago there were still many Viennese who had been grey for many a year and who went into raptures about Brahms because the famously murderous Olympian had been so friendly to them. When he visited us I sat peacefully on his lap and listened fascinated to the long discussions between father and my »adopted grandfather,« often interrupted by one of the two of them playing a short piece on the piano to underline his point of view.

I remember evenings on which Brahms, right in the middle of a conversation, would leave his coffee and cigar forgotten and sit down at the piano.

One of these episodes concerned Anton Bruckner, Brahms' arch-rival after Wagner's death. Since Brahms knew that my father was also Bruckner's friend, he made it a habit never to mention his best enemy in our house unless the topic was broached by someone else.

On that evening father had made a somewhat tired attempt at bringing the two rivals together. »In the end Schubert is a mutual basis for you both, Johannes – you've got to admit that!«

Brahms, without saying another word sat down at the piano and paraphrased indicatively a few initial passages from Bruckner's Fourth Symphony.

»In a sense, you're probably right, Jacob,« said Brahms and closed the lid of the piano. »I believe poor Bruckner wrote the symphony up to this point in his sleep and dreamed of Schubert while doing it. It didn't turn out badly at all but he woke up far too early …« Here he opened the lid again and then began to play with undisguised abhorrence – »Yes, he woke up. There he remembered that he is really a Wagnerian and then the rest of the symphony became a dreadful mess.« …

EUGEN GROSS

(∗ 1933)

Josef Plečnik on his way to world-wide fame

The city of Graz represents an oft-forgotten, important station on the journey of the Slovenian architect Josef Plečnik towards international standing. With its openness to southern influences, it attracted the young man from a Ljubljana cabinet maker's family in the years 1888–1892. Here he attended the Applied Arts

Department of the [King and Emperor] National College of Crafts founded in 1876. He was led to architecture by his teacher, Prof. Leopold Theyer who built many things in Graz. His further training as one of Otto Wagner's students at the Vienna Academy gave him the basis from which to achieve his initial successes as a young architect in the international metropolis of Vienna. The subtle Zacherl house and the remarkable Church of the Holy Ghost reveal his feeling for plasticity. In both furniture and applied arts and crafts design he devoted himself to sensitive details. Jan Kotěra, his friend and fellow-student under Otto Wagner, brought him to the School of Arts and Crafts in Prague where he taught his students a highly ethical view of architecture. As a result, the first President of the Czechoslovakian Republic, Tomáš Masaryk, commissioned him with the re-building and extension of his residence, the Hradschin. After the founding of the Faculty of Architecture in the Technical University of Ljubljana he was offered a chair in that institution in his home city. He worked there until his death in 1957. It was in this city, above all, that he devoted his undiminished creative powers to the countless public buildings and city facilities which still characterise the city that is the capital of Slovenia to this day. Plečnik's preference for classical, elementary base forms, combined with a visionary conception of space make him into one of the founding fathers of 20th century modernism. As acknowledgement of this position, the Centre Pompidou devoted a retrospective to him in 1986. Graz can thank Plečnik for furnishing a villa in the Geidorf Quarter where this »hidden Jugendstil bloom« is still blooming right up to the present.

KATHARINA PRATO

(1818–1897)

Grazer Rusks

Make a dough as for milk bread without egg yolks, but add whipped egg whites from 2 eggs, knead the dough well until it has air bubbles, place on the board and roll it out into a sausage form, cut into egg-sized pieces and roll out to finger thick sausages. Then make them into snail-shaped circles, place close together on a baking tray (placing the end of each sausage downwards) and in this manner form two loaves. Cover these loaves with a cloth and allow to rise, brush with water and place in a hot oven, brushing with water when they are half baked and also when they are finished. When they have sat for a day, cut them into pencil thin slices with a large, sharp knife. They should be covered on both sides with powered sugar in a bowl (for the amount of dough mentioned it will be around 400grams). They should be places on top of each other and left like that for about an hour. After the sugar has become moist the slices should be placed on a baking tray and roasted in a hot over until both sides are nicely browned. Place on top of each other and leave to cool.

For 1 1/2 litres of flour, take 40 grams of yeast which you to stir together with milk and a little flour and allow to rise, add 70 grams of sugar, powdered aniseed, a pinch of salt, 70 grams of butter or beef lard and enough milk to make a firm dough which is not to be beaten but kneaded in a bowl like bread dough. Do this until it starts to get air bubbles and when stretched, to stick a little to the hands. (You can also add one egg yolk to the mixture). Then place the dough on the board which has been sprinkled with flour, knead it through once again which will make bread with fine holes, form it into a loaf, place in a rectangular basket which has been lined with a flour-sprinkled cloth (a round loaf is made by putting it in a round basket or a bowl), cover it with a cloth and give it time to rise. Thereafter turn it out onto a greased baking tray which has been dusted with flour, baste with cold milk, bake and then baste with warm milk.

Or: take 1 1/2 litres flour, 400ml. full cream, 30grams yeast, 150 grams sugar, one egg, aniseed and salt.

WALTER KOSCHATZKY

(∗ 1921)

The never particularly conformist capital

Graz, never particularly conformist as the capital of
Styria, experienced an awakening around the turn of
the century as did other cities as well. The »quagmire
in a provincial backwater,« as Adalbert von Drasenovich
described it in 1900, might have been gloomier than
elsewhere after the great social, economic and hu-
manitarian renewal of the first half of the century
waned. In any case it proved to be tougher, more du-
rable and of considerable persistence. While Vienna
approached the radical movement (stretching from
Klimt's Secession to the Wiener Werkstätte) with social aversion but despite that moulded it into a style
of its own representing the empire's metropolis, Graz
proved to be hostile to a similar movement introduced
by Gurlitt and Drasenovich (one has to »steer with the
high-running waves of the current of European artistic life …«). If Gustav Klimt had formulated the Austrian answer to the challenges of his time – Austrian,
only to the same extent that Viennese society claimed
to be Austrian – then Graz would have made a much
stronger connection with the »New Art« from Munich. The relationship to Munich is, however, older.
For more than a generation the most talented Styrian
painters had looked to it for their education, had
found their calling there and their success … The
breakthrough of Jugendstil in Graz would be effected,

181

then, by the newcomer from Munich, Schad-Rossa
with a peculiar analogy in the musical sphere to Richard Strauss, who in 1901 and in the years thereafter,
put on successful performances finally culminating
in 1906 with the sensational premiere of »Salome.«
This earned Graz the title awarded it by Hanslicks of
»Richard Strauss' eternally loyal capital.«

WILHELM KIENZL

(1857–1941)

The Austrian Premiere of Salome
in Graz, 1906

Apart from the mastery which characterises it, Strauss's
art is first and foremost an art of nerves in the narrow-
est sense of that word because in some way, all art is
like that. The composer's compulsion pushes him so
far that at times he consciously repudiates all the
gods of art, getting carried away and going as far as
the realms of organised noise. I remember the runs of
ninths accompanying the words »Something terrible
will happen,« following the dominant seventh accords
on the word »crush,« on the collision of a naked B
major and D minor at the words »Order him to be silent,« (or should one here say something oracular
about the counterpoint of keys and musical scales?)
Can one – I ask myself – designate a process like that
as a misuse of artistic means? I think one will have

to resist something of this nature because one has to keep the artist's purpose in mind at all times. An impressionist painter nowadays is not prohibited from mixing any colour at all or using it in any way he likes as long as he achieves the desired effect. Why should impressionistic musicians not have the same freedom?

There is, however, another question – whether the goal he is striving for is worth the cost.

But can one dictate the material an artist can choose from and the methods he uses to achieve his ends? Everyone is free to be enthusiastic or to reject it.

Thus the only thing that one can justifiably accuse an artist of is *inconsistency*. Is there a greater (or, admittedly, more cruel) consistency than that exhibited by Strauss in his *Salome* ? Certainly not, this consistency is truly ironclad; here there is not even a glance to the left or right. Doesn't that alone demand respect? His score can only put one person or another in a bad mood because it contains intentions and nothing but intentions. Without doubt, one can assert that this creation shows not the slightest trace of naivety and that is the only thing that leads me to doubt the greatness of this art. Up till now no great art has had such a *complete absence of naivety*. In this respect Wagner, who was so extremely *purposeful,* appears to me childlike when compared to Strauss. Is it not a notion bordering on genius to have Herod sing in A minor (!) accompanying the harmonies of the two Nazarenes – as they tell of the wonder of Jesus – in A flat major? It is easy to see the intention behind this. This is the way Herod is supposed to be confronted with a higher world completely foreign to him, one which he cannot enter since it is completely closed to him. Similar things which many would regard as musical deadly sins abound in the »Salome« score. Alongside this there are parts of great clarity and accessibility which have the simplest harmonic relationships to each other. Thus, the word »beauty« is repeatedly underscored by Strauss with the tonic triad, something he apparently considers to be the most appropriate representation for it. His talent for combination knows no bounds for the ugly and the horrifying although, under certain conditions, even the used-up (and thus from the moderns carefully avoided) diminished 7th to express terror is not to be despised. Strauss also made the role of the God-inspired seer Jochanaan who, alone in »Salome« represents the moral weltanschauung in opposition to the world of depravity, into a musical carrier of simple greatness and natural feelings. Its tonal expression is made entirely of common harmonies. How sublime the music which accompanies Jochanaan's rise out of the cistern, the ceremonial stride of the person dedicated to God, the unapproachable, the protected! With these notes even that most daring of musical innovators, Strauss, admits that the expression of the sublime is unattainable without simplicity …

HANS VON DETTELBACH

(1900–1976)

Peter Rosegger, Wilhelm Kienzel and »Salome«

It came to a meeting between Richard Strauss and Peter Rosegger in Kienzel's house and a delightful story resulted, one that Kienzel himself told me. Strauss, the Bavarian, tried to win the Styrian for his work. He invited him to attend the performance of »Salome.« Rosegger resisted, but after Strausss had sent him admission tickets allowed himself to be persuaded to attend the performance. We may imagine his feelings. Next morning Kienzel heard Rosegger's come up to his doorstep. He rushed forward to greet him. The only thing Rosegger had to say to Kienzel was »Thank you very much for your »The Evangelimann« This was his full judgment with regard to »Salome.« Kienzel himself expressed his opinion in a review which is worth reading. It's tone is moderate but it contains phrases such as »almost shameless glorification of sexual psychopathology,« »organised sound,« »nerve art,« »no trace of naivety« and »without greatness.«

ERNST DECSEY

(1870–1941)

»Salome«

Soon there was great agitation in the city. Sides were taken, divisions, pub philosophers were buzzing around curious about the events surrounding the opera house. Big posters and newspaper reviews worked together and breached the walls of permanent resistance. The citizenry found out that the orchestra had been enlarged, part of the stalls taken over, that Richard Strauss himself had been invited. Ninety musicians! There was an arrogance in the number that was provoking. Was this opera twice as good as a »Lohengrin« that could be made with forty-five? Scandal … … … … … … The great evening arrived. »First Austrian performance of the newest work by Richard Strauss.« Visitors came from all over the province; critics came from Vienna as well as press, reporters and foreigners. The streets »surged« and Cavar's (he was at the time the director of the theatre) vision was fulfilled – three more than sold out performances. Receptionists groaned, hoteliers reached for their safe keys. An extraordinary number of curtain calls, jubilation, praise heaped on Strauss and the singers, for everyone. However, blows rained down on my back. Whatever it was they didn't understand, whatever they didn't like, they took it out on me. Duty scapegoat. A flood of letters buried me. »Idiot!« »Imbecile!« I was often called that in them. People of gentle disposition relieved pressure by scolding, those who were a little more robust accused me of corruption. »How much did you get to stand up for the swindle of an opera …?« That was the motive that came up again and again. Strauss would not have been able to raise that much. That you could support something with body and soul, help a new man with everything you had, did not get through the thick heads of these writers. »How much did you get for it …?« I'd probably been paid by the deceased Anton Bruckner and the deceased Hugo Wolf as well.

»A swindle of an opera!« The Philistines resisted the new picture behind this open umbrella. That an artist would need use the complicated circumlocution of a score to perpetrate a swindle and not the primitive methods preferred by business customs or the mutual dirt slinging employed by the normal citizens was also something they couldn't get through their heads. It was a long time before it dawned on them, but finally I was victorious. I thanked Strauss for a long time for the opportunity to get beaten up, to defend myself and to pay them back.

ALMA MAHLER-WERFEL

(1879–1964)

Gustav Mahler at the premiere of »Salome«

Mahler and I travelled to Graz in May for the Austrian premiere of »Salome,« to hear it there because Mahler had not been successful in clearing this work with the censor's office in Vienna. Even his suggestion of renaming Jochanaan, Baalschell was not accepted, yes, Mahler almost raised it to the level of a question for the cabinet. We found Strauss waiting for us in Hotel »Elefant.« He immediately suggested a car trip for the afternoon, to the waterfalls at Gollinger. Right after lunch we clattered off. It was after some rain, everything was soggy, the car skidded around. It didn't bother Strauss. When we got to a small inn an opulent snack was ordered and then we walked to the waterfalls. It was so beautiful that we couldn't tear ourselves away. At last we felt hungry and sat down again at the little wooden tables. But there it was again so comfortable that Strauss didn't want to leave for anything in the world.

»So what, they certainly can't start without me. They'll just have to wait.« He had a ferocious sense of humour. At last it began to get cool and as dusk drew on, Mahler jumped up and said, »Good, if you don't come along, I'll go and conduct for you.« That helped. Strauss stood up slowly and while Mahler encouraged the chauffeur to hurry, Strauss held him back. It appeared as if Mahler had Strauss' lack of authorial jitters but perhaps Strauss was not nearly as calm as he would have liked us to believe, perhaps he was very excited and hid it behind frivolity.

Despite the fact that a Christian Socialist scandal was feared in the morning after the very successful evening Strauss came to us at breakfast and began to reproach Mahler, »He took everything e.g. the opera – the whole shebang – too seriously, he should take care of himself ... Nobody gives a fig if he had worn himself out. A pigsty like that, that didn't even want to put on »Salome« – no, there was nothing to be said for it.«

Basically he was right. I always had that opinion. Despite the fact that every note he wrote was important to me, I was indifferent to his no doubt exemplary work in the opera. I *knew* even then that everything reproduced is ephemeral, his productions in contrast eternal.

Mahler was wont to say: »Strauss and I dig in separate shafts from different sides in the same mountain. We'll certainly meet at some point.«

Mahler and I stood in the corridor on our journey back to Vienna as was our habit; nature fresh after the heavy rain. We talked about what »success« is and its fallacies. Beside us stood an old gentleman who was obviously listening and he suddenly interrupted the conversation. It was Peter Rosegger. Mahler denied the reality of success. After all, we were coming from the Salome premiere. There had been much jubilation but nevertheless we were convinced that there was, at most, one in a hundred who had (perhaps) understood the music and who carried the rest of the herd along with them. And what about us? Were we not filled with doubts even during the performance itself; doubts about the choice of material, the music for the dance which we disapproved of, about so many things in spite of all the mastery. Suddenly the public decided it was a success. With what right and *who* had made the decision? Rosegger was of the opinion the voice of the people was the voice of God. So now we asked the question: the people through time or the people of the time? He was a jovial, loveable old gentleman, very rounded inside, harmonious and healthy. Almost the complete opposite to Mahler, the *restless*. He felt superior to Mahler, but Mahler did not feel inferior to him.

PETER ROSEGGER

(1843–1918)

Letter to Gustav Mahler

Doctor Peter Rosegger
Krieglach, 4. 7. 1910

Dear Sir,

I remember our encounter in the railway carriage well
and our conversation about the value of lack of value
of applause from the public. I cannot remember, however, your mentioning a paradox.

I think we had both agreed that the applause of the
masses is not worth much, but that it is, especially in
theatre, indispensable in refreshing the artist's nerves.
And that it is expedient for the public itself because
it helps them warm to increased ability to concen-
trate. By the way, your 3rd symphony did not just produce applause but rather it touched the heart, something which, if you weren't actually present, could
best be heard outside the theatre.

While I enjoy my summer holidays this year from
the invalid's bed, I hope you, my dear sir, will be enjoying yours in the high mountains and, if necessary,
relaxing in preparation for new creativity.

With my hearty congratulations,
your

Dr. Peter Rosegger

THOMAS MANN

(1875–1955)

What a talented skittle-club friend

I said that Adrian returned to the place to which an
impertinent ambassador had abducted him. But now
you see that it did not happen so soon. For a whole
year the pride of his spirit resisted the wound he had
received and it was always a kind of consolation to me
that his collapse in the face of the naked impulse
which had maliciously affected him did not really
lack all mental concealment or human ennoblement.
I see something like that in every *fixation* of desire
on a particular and individual target, whether crude
or otherwise; I see it in the moment of *choice* even if
it is involuntary and brazenly provoked by its object.
Love undergoes a visible purge as soon as the impulse
has a human face however anonymous or despicable
it is. And it may be said that Adrian returned to the
place because of one person: the one who burned his
cheek with a touch, the »dark« one in the cardigan
with the large mouth, who had approached him at the
piano and whom he called Esmeralda; it was her he
looked for there – and it was her that he did not find.

The fixation, as disastrous as it was, had the effect
that he left this place after his second, voluntary visit
in the same state as after the first, involuntary one but
not without having determined that the woman who
had touched him was present. It also had the effect

that, under the pretence of music, he went on a relatively long journey in order to find his heart's desire. At that time, May 1906, the Austrian premiere of Salome took place in Graz, the capital of Styria, under the direction of the composer.[*] Some months earlier Adrian had travelled with Kretzschmar to Dresden to see the first performance ever and he explained to his teacher and the friends he had meanwhile made in Leipzig that he wished to take this festive opportunity to hear the happy revolutionary work once again since, although its aesthetic sphere in no way attracted him, he was naturally interested in the musical and technical relationships and especially also as a musical setting of a prose dialogue. He travelled alone and it cannot be said with any certainty that he carried out his declared intention of going from Graz to Pressburg,[**] possibly also from Pressburg to Graz; or whether he only feigned his stay in Graz and limited his stay to Pressburg, called Pozsony in Hungarian. Actually, it was in a house there that the one whose touch he wore had ended up since she had had to give up her post for the sake of a course of treatment in a hospital and he was driven to find her in her new place ...

Adrian returned to Leipzig and talked of the compelling work of opera he had allegedly heard again and he had possibly heard it again, with amused admira-

---

[*] Richard Strauss
[**] Bratislava

tion. I can still hear him say, »What a talented chap,«[*] referring to its author, »the revolutionary as Sunday's child, impertinent and accommodating. Never were the avant-garde and guaranteed success so close together. Plenty of affronts and dissonance – and then good-natured compromises, reconcilement with the petit bourgeois and letting them know that it wasn't meant as bad as all that …but a successful work, a successful work …«

STEFAN ZWEIG

(1881–1942)

Hitler's Goliard Years

As Strauss himself told me, even in his goliard years in Vienna Hitler somehow laboriously scraped together some money to travel to Graz and be present at the premiere of Salome and showed him demonstrative respect. Apart from Wagner recitals, at all those formal evenings in Berchtesgaden there were almost only Strauss songs. For Strauss, participation was much more deliberate. With his artist's egotism which he always openly and calculatedly displayed, he was indifferent to every regime. He had served the German Emperor as musical director and arranged

---

[*] the word used is »Kegelbruder« meaning, literally »skittle-club friend.«

military marches for him, then he had been musical director to the court of the Austrian Emperor in Vienna and equally persona gratissima in the Austrian and German republics. To be particularly co-operative with the National Socialists was vital to him because according to their calculations he was deeply in debt. His son had married a Jewess and he must have been afraid that the grandson he loved above all else would be thrown out of school as scum. His new opera was burdened down with me, his earlier operas by Hugo von Hofmannsthal who was not »pure Aryan.« His publisher was a Jew. To him it appeared that much more imperative to gain support and this he did in the most dogged manner. He conducted wherever and whenever the new rulers wanted, he wrote an anthem for the Olympic Games and at the same time wrote me incredibly candid letters about his lack of enthusiasm for the commission. In reality, as far as his artistic sacro egoismo was concerned, he only worried about one thing and that was that to preserve his work in its vitality and effectiveness and, above all, to see that the new opera which was particularly close to his heart was staged.

HELMUT W. FLÜGEL

(∗ 1924)

Nobel Prize Winners

When Wegener[∗] went from his flat to his institute his route passed the institute of Fritz Pregl, winner of the 1923 Nobel Prize for chemistry, awarded for his development of the microanalysis of organic material; passed the windows behind which Felix Machatschki worked as an assistant and who, a little later, would discover the principles of silicate structure. He then went passed the institute in which Otto Loewi worked as Professor of Pharmacology and who had got the 1936 Nobel Prize for the discovery of the chemical transference of nerve impulses. Inside his own institute building he encountered Viktor Hess, Professor of Experimental Physics who received a Nobel Prize for the discovery of cosmic radiation in the same year as Loewi.

[∗] Alfred Wegener (1880–1930) became world famous for his theory of continental drift.

OTTO BREICHA

(∗ 1932)

About Wilhelm Thöny, painter
(b. 1888 in Graz, d. 1949 in New York)

With his re-immigration to his Styrian home a great
deal changed for Thöny in a fundamental way. In any
case his art changed, as the works that were made in
Graz bear witness. In other respects as well he threw
himself into the artistic and social life of Graz with
renewed élan. As early as 1923 Thöny initiated the
founding of the Grazer Secession on the model of
those in Berlin, Vienna and Munich. Together with
his fellow painters Fritz Silberbauer, Alfred Wicken-
burg, Axel Leskoschek, Hanns Wagula and the sculp-
tor Hans Mauracher it was their intention to breathe
new life into Graz's artistic life, a goal which was
presently realised. The Grazer Secession exhibitions
became high points, not only as art events, but also
as part of the social life of the city. It was not for nothing that Wilhelm Thöny was elected the first president of association ... His manifold activities in Graz
did not only serve the Secession but also himself. In
July 1929 he was awarded the title of professor. He
became a contributor to the most respected magazines
in Germany such as »Jugend« and »Querschnitt.«
There were Thöny exhibitions in leading galleries in
Austria and Germany as well as in Prague and New
York. In 1930 Thöny was one of the first Austrian
artists to be awarded the National Prize for Art.

RICHARD RUBINIG

(1914–1992)

Paul Celan

Celan got an invitation to Graz he was happy to accept. The visit was to repeat itself often. I had already got to know him at Jene's in Vienna by the time I turned up at Altanplatz along with my old friend Gustav Manker, the long-time director of the Viennese Volkstheater. Manker wanted to convince the painter to make the scenery for the theatre. Celan was present and was free and unaffected. His appearance was pleasing, his voice pleasant. One might have believed him to have a cheerful disposition, he made jokes and was able to be concerned with simple things. In Graz we got to know each other better. He specially liked visiting the house of the painter Kurt Weber whose work he valued. The pictures of Hans Bauer and Hans Nagelmüller also aroused his interest. Anything to do with literature got his immediate attention. He was courteous in his dealings with everything literary even if he didn't like it, which was usually the case. That was uncommon. On the other hand his friend and partner Max Hölzer could be quite sharp and aggressive when he didn't agree with something. In that case Celan sometimes suggested he look at things from another perspective.

In Kurt Weber's circle theoretical questions about lyrical poetry were often discussed. Hölzer was totally committed to André Breton while Celan dreamt of a

»distant poem« which had »no precursors« and which existed as an absolute by and for itself. He also considered that that linguistic apparatus of Surrealism and its symbolism was too cumbersome. According to him the pure poem had »no references,« »no background,« »no meaning,« indeed nothing which could be interpreted using other words. Stéphane Mallarmé who was generally admirable, had reached the frontiers of the upper regions, the final circle of light had remained closed to him, however. The poem that could only be « a poem in and for itself« would be a gift from heaven and exactly the opposite of what Gabriele D'Annunzio meant with his »Poema Paradisiaco.« A poem which is a poem for itself is not transparent but opaque. Opacity is the true character of poetry. It was only with Celan's the later books of poetry such as »Atemwende« and »Fadensonnen« had come out that we knew what the poet had meant.

Celan, who for some years alternated between living in Vienna and Paris, got a foothold in France again; he had become a French citizen and had married the graphic artist Gisèle Lestrange. In 1953 he accompanied her in making his last visit to Graz. Max Hölzer was a judge in the district court in Voitsberg at the time where he was in charge of the Department of Punishment. He lived with his wife Rudja (to whom he was indebted for his knowledge of the finer points of the French language) and a horde of children in Schloss St. Johann ob Hohenburg. His duties brought him into contact with the small-time thieves and ruffians of life. He was sorry for them all. There was not a judge who delivered milder sentences. The High

Court in Nelkengasse was often astounded to read Holzer's grounds, which they did with suppressed smiles but also understanding.

It was a beautiful summer day as Holzer and I drove with Celan and his Gisèle to St. Johann. The sooty railway was still in use. The Styrian meadows rejoiced in glimmering green and there were swallows and butterflies everywhere. We talked about Frederico García Lorca about whom I could claim a certain expertise though Gisèle, who understood Spanish, took part energetically. Next day Holzer, along with his guests from Paris, paid a visit to the painter Fritz Aduatz in Tregist. That was my last encounter with the poet who gradually became famous throughout Germany.

The first issue of the »Surrealist Publications« which had been so arduous to produce attracted attention but remained known only to a small circle of people. The elite of the Paris School was represented here – from Breton and Césaire to Victor Brauner and Yves Tanguy. The intention of producing a regular magazine could not be realised. A second issue appeared after an interval and was published by Èditions Surréalistes in Paris with contributions by Breton, Max Ernst, Hans Arp and Antonin Artaud. Rudolf Pointner. Franz Rogler had graphics in it. This issue number 2 never appeared in the bookshops and nowadays is not to be found anywhere.

Our connection to Celan was maintained for a time even after his move to Paris. When »Sezession Graz,« under the lively leadership of Rudolph Pointner, planned the publication of an art portfolio which would only contain original contributions we turned to Celan and asked him for a poem. He sent me a four-line work that referred to a picture by Van Gogh. He refused, in a friendly way, to make the hand-written multiples which would be required to go with the original drawings and watercolours and give the port-folio character on the grounds that it was really too boring for him. So it was Pointner, who had shone in his youth as a man of letters that produced this poem for all the portfolios issued in 1961. It runs:

Raven-swarmed wave of wheat –
Which sky blue? The lower? Upper?
Late arrow which sped from the heart –
Stronger twanging. Closer burning. Both worlds.

WALTER KOSCHATZKY

(* 1934)

A Picture by Paul Klee

One day back then (it was 1958) – and it is this in particular that should be rescued from oblivion – it came to a Grazer cultural ›peculiarity‹. The Urania Circle for Art and Philosophy were called on to accept a public challenge. It was intended, it was said, to hold a big public event in which a mock trial of mod-ern art would take place before an audience. It took place, in fact, in the Stephaniensaal. The prosecutor,

201

witnesses, defence and trial were to put on a great show. That happened and it became a shameful scandal. However, one didn't have to look for long to find out which way the wind was blowing. All too frequently echoes of degeneracy and distance from the volk could be heard, from the simple people's healthy common-sense feeling for art and last, but by no means least, a loss of reality, goodness and beauty was cited. The demand that all such pseudo-art smears should be prohibited was revealing and particularly concise. Georg Janoska had the thankless task of mounting a defence. He argued against the stupid attacks in a very controlled manner, highly intellectualised, perhaps too highly, so that his highly differentiate logic was almost not understood by the public. On the other hand the primitive slogan-spouting prosecutors were greeted with cheers and one had to be content to leave the room without substantial injury. Everything disappeared under a wave of whistles and jeers, derision and laughter. I don't think that anything of nature has ever happened anywhere else. We can only hope that something like this would not be possible today, nor in the future ...

Once in the fifties, when I was already the director of the Neuen Galerie I remember receiving a newspaper cutting directly from the desk of the governor of the province which reported a street survey about art. The evaluation of a postcard of one of Paul Klee's pictures shown to people elicited a positive response from not more that 0.6 per cent of them. Although that was not to say that they had said that they liked the picture. It was a long way from that. It was rather simple – they just agreed to call it *a work of art*. All the rest, 99,4 that means, didn't do that. So, 0,6! The provincial governor had written in the margin, » difficult to argue for a bigger budget!«

ALFRED KOLLERITSCH

(∗ 1931)

If you could ward off the love of this city, you would leave it

We wanted life, not the idea. Who were we? Back then almost none of us had been on the other side of the country's border. Graz was foreign territory that we conquered, (a place) we made human as if we could forget the war that way. Day after day, night after night they hammered into us how necessary it was. We belong to a unity, they said, to the empire and then the club-foot slunk through our dormitories, the educator who learned the nature of the Germans from Braille and picked up the scent of the unrestrained (individuals) in our breed and said that anyone who did not masturbate could not be a German youth (we were almost of the opinion that the all-understanding Führer must approve). His attempt to penetrate our wildness was exploited by those in power to send him to the scaffold (when I wanted to research his life and death around 1970, his file did not exist anymore, the filing cabinet had been emptied but not the psyche). When he was taken away before our eyes, it was little different to when a mother smoothes out a tablecloth.

The same opinion could be heard even there where nothing was said about the political events of the time. The educators beat, the teachers threatened, the means of learning were mean of intimidation. The written progress reports emphasised the condition of the body and hammered the pedagogical truth into us with rules of order (the need of direction) in whose light the material was to be formed. I looked at one teacher as I would a puzzle, the subsequent mayor of the City of Graz, the socialist Dr. Eduard Speck. It was said about him that he thought *differently* to the others, that he was politically suspect. We didn't know what that difference was. He was silent about it. He taught Latin grammar. Alongside him the old teachers who had already retired but had been recalled into service seemed to be timeless and useless for the future they taught us.

It's like this: if you could defend yourself against your own love of the city you would leave it. Go away from its size, away from the fatal relationship of everything with everything else, away from being permanently known, out of the game of being open and out of the game of isolating yourself, each of which is a game about winning a place in the hierarchy in accordance with local rules of »possession.« In a large city unity of identity gets lost, the dominance of those who believe they make up the city. Graz is (was?) a city which staged a rising by itself. It is against this that *reciprocated love* is directed, the turmoil of wishing that Graz can be freed from itself so that it can learn to regard itself as other than it is. Reciprocated love is not love-hate, reciprocated love is a wishful love which anchors itself on the hope that the place opens up to be a home, that its self-understanding is broken open and that it tears false labels off. To name but one example, the city has to give up raising Robert Stolz to the position of a spiritual mayor. Reciprocated love is a fight for the city and against the privilege of those who incessantly reproduce the timeless wishes of their fellow citizens. Reciprocated love is more effective than an absolute morality and self-opinionatedness of simple negation. We have to fight for reciprocated love even as we live with the others and, if we are honest, we are often self-satisfied at this kind of togetherness. It is here that it is at its most entangling, when you meet the so-called ordinary people in the pub, take a seat with them and notice, from their voices, the abyss they have to cope with in their own way. Certainly this occurs the world over, but its concrete nature is in accord with each place. Every place has its own province of limited and reachable happiness, each its own meaning, experience of the world. To enter it means to go beyond it or to become its prisoner. This is where responsibility begins, at the very latest. Whoever approaches this suppressed happiness of people tempted by needs; whoever makes their happiness the measure of all things and himself to the voice of the people, is someone who forces them deeper into their hopelessness and that is just as risky a game as if you would try to incite them with ideas of general validity. To treat Grazers like that would mean that they were compelled to remain even more strictly inside their borders. Reciprocated love wants Grazer to step outside of their borders, not like refugees who make it easy on themselves, changing nothing but moving away. Reciprocated love wants the Grazer to become something else where he is. Its facticity must crack open the mask, the narrowness, its lack of sophistication, its obstinacy, superficial heart, lack of fantasy, its self-satisfied, reluctance derived from superficial pleasure. Reciprocated love seeks out the discrepancies in the naturalness »of the necessary failure of passionate efforts towards identity.« What a dream – the least that could come from this self-preservation run wild is irony.

GERHARD M. DIENES

(∗ 1953)

The Old Town in Danger

During this time, the old part of Graz was in serious danger of being badly damaged by thoughtless demolition and alterations. Thus the former Palais Khuenberg, for example, (Sackstrasse 18, nowadays the City Museum) with its three-part, tiled roof should have given way to a multi-storey car park. However, in 1972 the action committee »Save the Old Town« was founded and in 1974 the Grazer Old Town Preservation Law was passed. Consciousness of the old town had been awakened. Now the old town's »roofscape« was seen as beautiful and worth protecting, the saddle-backed and hipped roofs were described and marketed to tourists. The picturesque tangle of roofs, the closely-packed houses, the long densely-built groups of houses and the multiply-articulated tiled roofs are, today, one of the most important attractions of the Grazer old town.

ERNST JANDL

(1925–2000)

»manuscripte«

vienna, 15. 4. 1967

1

»manuscripte« is the only austrian magazine consistently contributing to international efforts towards a new literature which is to say, a literature that is, in principle, art, in opposition to entertainment or educational literature. »manuscripte« is therefore acknowledged, read, discussed, and supplied with contributions from literary centres such as frankfurt, stuttgart, berlin, prague and london. they make new literature from austria known abroad, and foreign literature known in austria. »manuscripte« offers a panorama of new literature, as compared to h.f. kulterer's magazine »eröffnungen« which is dedicated to producing more limited special numbers; the successor to »wort in der zeit« and the magazine »literatur und kritik,« »manuscripte« is years ahead as a documentation of the austrian modern movement.

2

»manuscripte« has particular merit in that it has published literary and theoretical texts from raoul hausmann who, as an 81 year-old today, enjoys an international reputation as a pioneer of the new literature and who, in his native country, has only been able to get a word through edgeways in »manuscripte.«

3

austrian literature exists only within the framework of german-language literature. to restrict oneself to austria, even when this abortive enterprise goes under the heading of »reflection,« would be the end of austrian literature. here, to create clarity, to keep the frame of reference the german language, to fetch authors such as bense, krolow, heissenbüttel, mon, dohl, borchers and all the others who form the basis of german literature and to harness them together with modern literary german- language writers in austria for the indispensable purpose of comparison, contrasting strengths and weaknesses, exchanging ideas, strengthening ties and promoting fertile frictions – all this was the function of the magazine »manuscripte« through the years, and it should continue to stay like that.

4

as long as this magazine is a lively as the literature it tries to publish, it cannot and should not avoid the shock that the content causes in some people; »manu-scripte« is not a mass circulation paper, its selection criteria for texts cannot, therefore, be measured against that of the latter but can certainly against that of the most respected german-language literary magazine, AKZENTE. its documentation of current american prose in issue 6/66, pages 501 to 544 of its 13th year provides impressive examples of modern american authors attempting an artistic processing of obscenity as an important part of linguistic reality and human experience. the attempts nowadays by artists all over the world to get to grips with obscenity artistically is carried out in the assumption that there is nothing which is outside of art as a matter of principle. to exclude this great and significant process because of timidity would be completely contrary to the concept of »manuscripte.« texts like this do not have anything whatever to do with pornography; pornography is a sector of entertainment and educational literature.

HANNS KOREN

(1906–1985)

Looking for A New Way in New World

The artist is no longer to be found in the lists of domestic servants of nobles and prelates, responsible for producing works for their wonder and representation; he is no longer the decorator of a bourgeois world, illustrating their sentimental feelings, heroic deeds and sensual impressions but he has become more of an accessory to or the compassionate accomplice of the times and its state. His works are documents evidencing his membership in it. With them he undertakes to search for a new way in a new world.

What is new is the integration of musical and scientific life and endeavours. This is the other thing our »steirischer herbst« has developed into by stages and which it will continue to develop more intensively than ever. Since it is the energies of the province and city and first and foremost those of the stage, lecture halls, studios, rehearsal rooms, sound studios and laboratories that are called upon to demonstrate what the province can achieve but also to show from which natural, historical and human provenance these energies come, it is they that represent the province in the today world and for posterity. It is because of this that the »steirischer herbst« is an image the province has of itself, a ceremonial proclamation and at the same time something worked for with diligence and enthusiasm.

The city's atmosphere itself, attractive with its unique buildings and squares, will be a huge stage, lit up by early autumn, just as Salzburg is an incomparable stage and just as the banks of Lake Boden offer an adaptable backdrop, the city scenery here will do the same. Nevertheless, it will not be simply the scenery in front of which foreign guests conduct and the Styrians themselves are but ticket collectors and stage hands. The children of the province have front-stall seats, the play is for them and they are part of the play ...

EMIL BREISACH

(∗ 1923)

There are ghosts going around

Statement of a Grazer taxi driver on the 13th October: » Yesterday evening I took two men to one of the worst nightclubs on Gries. On the way they continually pulled ghosts to pieces.«

»An act of desperation: suicidal leap in theatre« – »Does it taste good? Drawing attention to the third world with bananas« – »Gomes: Orders to shoot rioters« – »Frequent changes of partner increases cervical cancer« – »Farmer's wife finds babies body in pond: murder« – »Building as environmental destruction: ruining Austria« – »250,000 people die on the roads every year ...«

I found these headlines in the »Kleinen Zeitung« on Sunday. I could cite the headlines from any other paper on any other day to the same effect. An intact world? Is that a reason for present-day authors who experience this for themselves and who search behind the headlines for the real stories, to write friendly comedies?

Wolfgang Bauer lives in this reality. He has subjected himself to one of the most radical forms of game in this »chaotic« world. The ascribed bourgeois roles are thrown off, social relationships torn apart. The suppressed characteristics of the human species reign supreme: uninhibited satisfaction of desires, sadism, self-destruction, perversity. In between there is a surfeit of reflections on dismay during a quest for a lost identity. The overtaxed state of awareness makes one sit up and take notice. Dreams, imagination, drunkenness and observation are transformed into reality. You force yourself in to the private life of others, change partners, assume another role. Humans, who take appearances for reality in order to survive, unleash his ardent pleasure in playing games: exoneration chess with beer bottles, trivial bourgeois dinner table games, the sudden checkmate of the victim on the sidelines: guilt as a reality that can never be escaped. Bauer describes what he has seen, heard or experienced. He registers this one reality. He does not mince his words. He doesn't make anything better than it is. His only moral stance is truth.

This naked openness is exactly where the anger of the righteous becomes incendiary. What do we have to do with this circle of flipped out, depraved degenerates; what do we have to do with these drinkers, these good-for-nothing parasites? The indignant reaction is so violent you have to assume Bauer has touched on a sore point. Perhaps shared blame and responsibility? Who or what has created this underground? Is the withdrawal from the circle of the law-abiding, normal citizens a purely arbitrary act? Are these young people an extreme symptom of lack of love, lack of contact, alienation from our behavioural patterns which are predicated on superficial prosperity? Do the headlines above, lined up one after another signalise a world that is so much better than theirs? Are we only so dismayed because someone tears open reality behind the headlines?

All the same the obscene language is not ours, it drags everything we hold holy through the dirt. At any rate, the vocabulary used was perfectly understandable. Why, actually? Do we also move in Wolfgang Bauer's world? Or does the jargon occur in our own environment? Which jokes do smart academics tell in the pub? Where do the lavatory scribbles come from in the pubs? Is it not the older generation which guarantee good sales of sex and porno mags? Why have the anonymous letter writers and callers suddenly discovered Wolfgang Bauer's vocabulary for themselves? Where does this secret pleasure in its use come from? Have the secret corners of the compost heap suddenly been opened up? In that case Bauer would not only lifted the sheets on his own circle! The double morality revealed here up and down the country is a good example from which to learn. The professors, men and women, who wonder if the piece is good for the young should interpret it better. All these effects it has uncovers things that were concealed. Confronted truth never hurt anyone. Our teenagers have no desire to orientate themselves on the ghosts that seem to be omnipresent lately.

GERHARD ROTH

(∗ 1942)

Helmut Qualtinger was attacked

Helmut Qualtinger was attacked in Graz for *Jugend vor den Schranken* in such a way that he decided never to go there again. He ...never set foot in Graz again. *Manuskripte* ... was confiscated ... Wolfgang Bauer, 1975, *Die Gespenster*, there the papers were full of readers' letters demanding that Bauer be sent to the workhouse. At that time measures were initiated against the Steierischen Herbst which attracted a notable 25,000 signatures ... They wanted a »regionalisation of the Steierischen Herbst« and poets such as Max Mell, Ottokar Kernstock and Paula Grogger – all sympathisers with the Nazi regime – were to be placed in the foreground.

PETER HANDKE

(∗ 1942)

I was srangely proud of him

There is no other country in which the writers regard
each other with such adversarial attitudes as in Austria. And if a few manage to become friends then, instead of preserving their individual perceptual apparatus, they immediately form a group, presenting
themselves as a gang with a standardised perceptual
schema which may be appropriate for a political
party, perhaps, but not for a writers. For the latter
there can be no pre-determined insights, nothing can
be regarded as a matter of course, no words put into
their mouths and nothing already thought through to
a conclusion. So Austrian literature cannot be seen
as a group of independent writers writing affably and
reasonably and perhaps (why not?) a little enviously,
presenting possible ways of living in society but more
like a teeming mass of people who have been humili-
ated and insulted. It is thus almost justified that the
public is only cognisant of that teeming mass. So, for
example, Franz Nabl, an important Austrian writer
(»Ödhof,« »Die Ortliebschen Frauen«), had to live to
be nearly ninety years old before he could escape
from the group which screened him off with whispered
and grumbled literature stories from we younger authors and, having made contact, he became one of us.
I, too, considered Nabl to be someone who could and
(above all) wanted to say nothing to me because of

what had been written and said about him. Certainly what I had read years ago of his work gave the impression of being mysterious and had remained in my mind and becoming stronger without me doing anything. I thought about him often and was depressed that those who admired someone – his »adherents,« – protected him so much that his work almost suffocated. In the story »Der kurze Brief zum langen Abschied« I then quoted him shamelessly from memory in describing my own childhood experiences – an environment which would burst at some point and the surroundings, the weather, the sun etc. would suddenly become a monster. That, however, I remembered, had also been also one of Franz Nabl's fundamental experiences … A few months ago I met him personally in his house in Graz with its beautiful wooden staircase which had been scrubbed to a light colour over the years. We drank a great deal of rowan schnapps until I fell into the grass in his garden. It was on his balcony that I read the lecture he had given in Graz in 1933 on modern literature and I was amazed at the friendliness and selflessness with which he came to terms with authors who must have been foreign to him. I looked at Franz Nabl and became animated in front of this old person although beforehand I had been afraid that I would not be able to say anything. I talked a lot and was strangely proud of him thinking that he had spent his whole life as a writer and was now listening to me full of dignity and kindness and was clinking glasses with me. He had offered my friends and I the most comfortable chairs and he himself sat on a stool. At first I wanted to refuse but then

I thought it right. I don't know if anyone will understand that. We should take the example of the individual writers and their works.

1972

ELIAS CANETTI

(1905–1994)

It embarrasses me

There are ever fewer cities that captivate you from their beauty alone. Graz very definitely belongs to them. I say this with a certain amount of timidity because you live here and so might consider my testimonial as superfluous when weighed against your experience. But I will say it anyway because I have to add something which I am, perhaps, more entitled to judge. This city, which preserved its form at a time of general destruction, has become a nerve centre of modern literature in the German language. The particular nature and great numbers of talented people who have emerged here in the last 10 to 15 years is astounding and no-one who has taken the fate of literature to heart can be indifferent to that. Movements like this naturally start small and if they do not get the understanding of those who can lend support, they must of necessity fizzle out or move to the larger cities where a part will be ground down before it even gets going. It requires not only openness but also a special degree of patience to accept something new because what would be new about it if it was not off-putting at first? In Graz there were supporters of this nature and as an observer who has been drawn back to the city time and again over the last 10 years I was more than a little impressed by their persistence and steadfastness. I have felt at first hand what it means to come into a city in which one is *heard*, where something like anticipation for intellectual things exists. A city in which examination and re-ordering of outmoded values happens continuously. In each generation there have to be those who initiate everything, who combine talent with audacity. Whether or not they are successful, traditional literature, including what is regarded as inviolable, would die a sad and academic death without their feelings for it.

Notwithstanding the pleasure I naturally feel, it makes me slightly embarrassed that the City of Graz, in which young talent abounds, awards me, a 70 year-old, the prize. It makes me happy that the prize is called after Franz Nabl.

I became convinced of Franz Nabl's significance quite young when I read *Ödhof* and some stories. Later many things got lost, I left Austria and didn't know if I would ever see it again. Then there was an Austria again and when I came to Graz in 1965 I visited Franz Nabl and felt strongly drawn to him. I saw him every time I came to Graz again. On a wonderful journey which one should really only describe in all its details, he did me the honour of showing me southern Styria. After that I gradually read all his books, a good number of which had been unknown to me. The feeling I had that the work had been pushed aside by those who should have known better began to depress me. Perhaps it has not been read properly sometimes, it is a truthful and stern oeuvre, not one that ingratiates itself. Please allow me a few words to tell you how I see it. Franz Nabl had the courage that few writers have, that few writers find present in themselves, the courage to treat death seriously. He did not avoid it, he saw it as it was and always confronted it in the fates of the characters he created. Unlike some of his famous Austrian contemporaries he did not allow himself to be caught in vain and indecent game with death. At the time he began to write it had become fashionable in literature to anticipate the threat under which we all live with seductive blandishments. He resisted that trend and remained loyal to his seriousness and his insights. The central figure of his first great novel, *Ödhof*, is a person who has to destroy everyone around him and derives his power from that. One can certainly call it a figure of power. In the private sphere this power is directed against those closest to him, his wife and child; precisely those who rely on being protected and are helplessly vulnerable. The reprehensibility of such an existence has never been questioned, we have only become really aware of its dangers recently. As a writer, and he is one of the greatest Austrian writers, Franz Nabl started from concrete situations and throughout his life he remained trapped in the individual and the concrete. He paid for his awareness of the destructibility of every single thing with melancholy. It

219

wasn't easy for him but he found the counterforce he needed to withstand the destruction early on. When he was young it was still possible for him to experience nature in all its forms as being intact. He surrendered himself to it with persistence and love but also with an unquenchable longing for precise knowledge. What he rendered into words and described seduced some into seeing him as a romantic but those who know his strengths and his sombre works know that it was also his nature to look for what was indestructible. Nowadays, as we experience the rapid destruction of everything in nature that seemed to be assured, we are aware that we have wrought destruction as much on ourselves as on nature. In this way, perhaps, we feel ourselves more affected by the other quality of his work – the incorruptibility with which he formed man's nature, his undoing.

GERHARD ROTH

(* 1942)

The »youngsters« were the nicest thing for him in his old age

We sat in his little sitting room, his wife cooked (very well!) and we talked. He liked it when I told him I enjoyed his books or individual stories. Then he would talk about them very precisely as if he wanted to make sure that I had read them closely. He spoke of politics a little awkwardly. I think it bothered him to talk about politics on its own without it being simultaneously bound up with his personal history.

When summer was over, we saw less of each other because I had to go to work again writing ›Großen Horizont‹ but we telephoned now and then and he also came to my play (›Lichtenberg‹) which he saw with a measure of astonishment, I think. I assume that he didn't like it very much. On Christmas Day Wolfi (Wolfgang Bauer), Fredi (Alfred Kolleritsch, Zankl (Horst), Gunter Falk, Holzinger (Alfred) and I visited him in his flat. He was happy to see us all and we drank a good Dirndl schnapps and suddenly he asked us whether we thought that even one page of his work »was worth anything.« It seemed to me that he had had to overcome his reticence in order to ask. Three weeks later he was dead. I saw him the day before he died. He lay in the second medical clinic of the Graz District Hospital and it was a murky, misty evening. His face was yellow and his cheeks had hollowed out and he had great difficulty breathing. He didn't want any of this to be noticed (without posturing) and asked me when we could ›down a beer‹ together again. I gave him my hand and he held it tightly the whole time I was there. For a while all you could hear was him breathing and now and then he gave a slight cough. Then at some point he said, »Don't forget me.« He also said that we ›young ones‹ had been the nicest thing to happen to him in his old age. I made a couple of jokes and he liked that. His face was so peaceful that I continued to entertain him in that vein. He collapsed suddenly and the beard stubble and the dark-coloured lips and the nervous hand on the bedcover made him look wretched. Next day Fredi and Wolfi went to visit him. He had just died as they opened the door.

WOLFGANG BAUER

(∗ 1941)

In the middle of driving snow

I came across Ionesco around 1960 in Graz. The cineaste Günter Straschek taught a course about the theatre of the absurd in the Urania. There were only four of us and on the first evening we read »Die kahle Sängerin« with separate parts. We only progressed slowly because we had to laugh so much. It was no longer a reading but an anticipatory glance at the next sentence and a howl, an unrestrained roar of laughter. The subsequent analysis restricted itself to a short banter. You could perhaps say that ... senselessness ... emptiness ... It was just a little alibi discussion that quickly slipped into a general position-finding and a laugh-about-it-again. Yes, that was the most extraordinary thing with Ionesco, his humour. Humour is his special quality, both personal and artistic. Fear, symbolism and senselessness are only the basis of the joke which is creative ...

When I was in Paris in 1961 I wanted, above all, to meet the master … It was a woman on the phone. I said that I was a poet from »Graz, Autriche,« and that I admired her husband and that I had to meet him. She said that her husband was working, I should please come at 2 o'clock … The woman led me into the kitchen where a strapping man in an overall, with sweating upper arms sat eating. The woman closed the kitchen door behind me.

It was a case of mistaken identity. The bull in the overalls was called Eugene Ionesco but he was – a plumber.

Ionesco had to laugh a lot at this story. I told it to him in the little liqueur pub, Haring's, in Graz while he stroked a dachshund belonging to the wife of a Graz plumber. After at least 15 large vodkas we stepped euphorically out onto Mehlplatz which Ionesco found Venetian. We stood immediately outside the house where twelve years before I got to know his plays. I knew how wonderful the meeting would be for me (and now, writing about it, it is again) but it was entirely literary. I couldn't identify the bundle of emotions his work had matured in me with the person of Ionesco himself and so we stood there in the middle of driving snow, laughing, the body of the poet and high above him, coming from the Graz Urania, a giggling which wiped everything else out – the »Die kahle Sängerin.«

ALFRED PAUL SCHMIDT

(* 1941)

The Great Classics of Graz or
A Hard Day's Night

When the Graz author has finished work, when he has
notched up a page of his great work, industrious as a
copper-plate engraver, he's always at work on a great
work, then he proceeds to relax into the arms of the
great classics of Graz, partly because of the »human
relations« but, above all, also because he doesn't
know what he should write tomorrow. Among local
contemporaries this is understood to mean a pub
crawl, its stations lined up through the night like the
berries of the deadly nightshade.

First of all, around six in the evening he goes to
HARING'S. There the honest boozers sit, bottle-
bashing pensioners and drinking mates partaking of
a subaltern sort of schnapps of local provenance.
Whisky, Scotch, bourbon, gin or whatever that stuff
from abroad is called, are imported foreign words.
The local authorial guild brings both remarkable
overseas ideas and word smiths here too, e.g. the honourable Ionesco, when they are asked by television to
document Styrian originality sitting in the lap of so-
phisticated modernism. When Dali is in Graz, he also
goes there. Otherwise a regular there is the famous
genius from Wolfi Bauer's »Gespenstern« ... Mr. or
Mrs. HARING lock up at seven.

Then the trail leads to MILD, a pub where painters and office workers begin or end the day, as appropriate. The pub is noted above all for Mr. Mild who claims to be a miserly Saxon from Siebenbürgen, but you can't tell that from the way he looks. Objectively he could be from any part of the world where people speak Saxon. You drink wine, beer, etc. there. Whoever has money eats something as well. Mantschari[*] number one.

Thereafter, you change places. The change is inspired by closing time. You go to LÜCKL'S. Apart from the poetic tone (which is why you order the fodder with »Herr Lückl, no a Schlückl«)[**] the Grazer city poet, Herwig Kreutzbruck, reigns here. His professional pseudonym: Herwig von Kreutzbruck. An impartial person who happened by would find out that the entire group of inmates has got into a powerful typhoon of nerve gas. Everyday is theatre of the absurd here. Herwig holds dark, incomprehensible speeches abounding with emperors, kings, knights and saints of all confessions. The most illustrious Greek and Christian medieval philosophers have to bear the brunt of the work when he wants to prove to someone that it is time for another bottle of red wine. To admit you didn't understand a single work would come close to defeatism. This is why everyone from the poet's circle attempts to fall into an equally ambiguous hermeticism, striving for magical darkness. So everyone understand each other quite well. Everybody can think what he wants to.

---

[*] Dialect, from Italian meaning ›to eat.‹

[**] »Mr. Lückl, another mouthful.«

Due to the guests' nervousness and absent mindedness a lot of things get knocked down and brave Mr. Lückl has long given up trying to clean the tables of their diverse spills. Which is why it is advisable for a visitor with a fastidious upbringing to carry a Wettex with him.

When midnight finally strikes, the ghosts fly to KODOLITSCH in Bürgergasse where all the left-wing students sit, gloriously drunk, debating their positions in the coming millennium. When you (also gloriously drunk) try to explain to them that the left and the psychedelic movement are brothers – and after twelve I usually belong to the second group – they argue as one man that these »way out where« methods just play directly into the hands of capitalism.

Frequently a ban is remains a real possibility at KODO'S . Every necromancer who does just a little bit of glass throwing is inevitably thrown out. But what can you do with the aggro when you're totally pissed?

At two it's off to the THEATERKAFFEE. There, everyone's thirsty but no-one has any more money. That's why the waiters have a difficult job. In winter it's easier, you can leave your coat as security and because of the freezing weather you redeem it as soon as possible.

The piano player, a very dignified elderly lady, patters her salon pieces into the smoke and noise-laden surroundings. You have to pay music tax for it. The burschenschaftler*, if there still is such a thing, find the music apposite to their way of life and I don't give a fig because you can be yourself there, say what you want, as if you had got a loan to help overcome an alcoholic's fate.

And that leaves just the SPOR BUFFET, a café that opens early and at four in the morning begins to digest what remains of the night. How you get there is one of these unfathomable questions that appears to invest the Grazer classic with para-kinetic abilities. As a matter of principle you drink in SPOR BUFFET on chalk-it-up credit. Nothing special happens there apart from programmed punch-ups but everybody is far gone, distracted, so you don't really notice. In order to describe the scene in loving detail and picturesquely it would require a sober observer with the qualities of a nineteenth century writer and that, quite clearly, is certainly not in keeping with the great Grazer classics at all. At some point, when no more money at all can be raised, Paul, the experienced and kindly waiter says, »That's enough for today.« »Think so?« says the covered-up writer, in order to keep face. As a finale, after you've mourned the fate of all the migrant workers present in the Russian way as part of the »human relations,« you have your corpse transferred to your home by taxi.

The spectre of a hangover and the accompanying nerve tremolo belongs to the postscript of the great Grazer classic, as does the acknowledgement of having had a wonderful night with wonderful people about which you can remember almost nothing. And that's why Grazer authors have no other choice but to invent.

---

* Strictly speaking, a student's duelling society.

LOJZE WIESER

(∗ 1954)

Franz, the Bookseller

Summer. An alternative event to the Bachmann readings in the Stadthaus, the former palatial residence of Kleinmeyer, the publisher. Sitting in a corner there is a stooped-over giant. We haven't seen each other for a long time. The books at Residenz Publishing lie in the distant past. Sad eyes, shaggy beard. We sit and drink for a long time. We talk about the bookshop in Graz. From writer to bookseller. We drink. Silence. Laugh a little. He tells me lovingly about his bookshop in the making. And about writing, which plagues him. About a shoemaker's apprentice. He smiles. I tell him about the birth of the publishing house. When I've written it, I'll come to you.

We sit even longer. Silently. Drinking. When we separate we wish each other good luck.

A final book appeared later, his old publisher. He couldn't do anything else he said with regret when we saw each other for the last time. And the bookshop? Sad eyes, black-grey shaggy beard.

Dedicated to Franz Innerhofer (1944–2002)

GERHARD MELZER

(∗ 1950)

Autumn Fragments
(Styrian Autumn 1988)

I live in the centre of Graz. I can only open my window without trepidation at night or at the weekend. The rest of the time the rattling and vibrating windows signal that outside the noise of the traffic roars. Quite apart from the fact that something other than fresh air would come in an open window.

I can also make an accurate picture of the how punctual the domestic airlines are. The roar and drone of the metal birds swarming out towards Zurich or Frankfurt often sweetens my awakening from the last dream of the night. Recently it certainly seemed as if the dream would never end. The hoot of a foghorn revealed what Ingeborg Bachmann already knew – that not only Bohemia but also Graz suddenly lay by the sea.

Strange bird calls and animal voices transported me into a world I have never been before. In Graz's Stadtpark the trees began to proliferate; the Schlossberg disappeared into a thicket of impenetrable jungle. In place of the familiar squirrels, gibbons swung through the branches and when they mated their lust hung in the air. At the main station sailing boats rocked in the wind and now and then a bell called for reflection from the Tempelbezirk* of Mariatrost. On the roads which linked the city jungle I didn't meet natives any more, only strange foreigners. I could not recognize even public figures or friends who should certainly have been familiar to me. There was nothing left for me to do except rediscover them for myself and they did the same. We explored each other like ethnologists and the results were amazing. I really couldn't say if we used our normal language, it is more than likely we howled like wolves while the foghorn continued undaunted to tell its tale of the disappearance of the world.

Just before Graz finally took on a completely different form, the dream ended. Some of the inhabitants had become afraid and with them the administrators of fear, the politicians. We don't need any foreign noises in the city, they said, they only confuse the people and in the end we don't know who we are any more and whether we are awake or dreaming. So we'll just be content with the sounds that we know. It is night time. I open the window. Almost nothing to be heard. My dream of a transformed Graz slowly fades into the silence. Slowly the jungle dies off, the gibbons sit sadly on ash-grey tree stumps and think about the crises in their relationships, the tankers on the main square empty their machine oil into the harbour. Tomorrow morning the window panes will be rattling again.

---

* Temple District

MATHIAS GRILJ

(∗ 1954)

Schizoid but relaxed

The anarchistic awareness of life in the Sixties and
Seventies flashes out of the epitaph to Harings, the
tiny pub, written by Wolfgang Bauer in 1990. From
those Sixties and Seventies when life was a dream
and what you could make of it, » As soon as you'd
opened the door you stepped onto a kind of stage,
slippery boards that represent the world here. You're
not left in peace because there was always something
approaching the Shakespearian going on. Tugged at,
laughing, shouting, cursing. Some maniac was always
staging a farce, over there someone was singing an
aria and in the back, in the ›poet's room‹ the phone
level was so loud that ... You were audience and lead
role at the same time. Creative and compulsive behaviour mixed into a volcanic cocktail. A sensation
had to happen every second, every sentence was
forged and directed. You were ruled by foreign laws.«
From the list of guests: Eugene Ionesco, Allen Gings-
berg, Hubert Fichte, Rolf Dieter Brinkmann, Oswald
Wiener, Wolf Wondratschek, Towje Kleiner, Attersee
... Why go out into the world when the world comes
in to you?

For Wolfgang Bauer himself, everything seemed so
easy. You almost can't tell when he is working. That
he had to be locked up in a hotel room because of

›Fieberkopf‹ and was only released when the novel was finished doesn't change the picture in any way. He can both abolish contradictions and allow them to co-exist. It has never posed a problem for him when something is and isn't at the same time. With great relish he demonstrates how you can abolish the border between art and life, he aestheticises life and integrates it into his art – both in the way he produces it and in the work itself that is very often a game within a game within a game.

MANFRED MIXNER

(∗ 1947)

LITERATUREGRAZ – a Reflection

... I have pictures and voices in me from relatives and acquaintances, friends and foes. In almost twenty years of absence I have created my own Graz from them and I no longer know (and no wish to know) whether it is really like that outside of my thoughts and feelings.

My aesthetic experience and my interest in the poetic were schooled in another Graz, I call it LITERATURE-GRAZ. I took part in the »business« here, starting from being a shy reader and listener, I became one of the organisers of the programme of literary events. From this closeness and on the basis of the supposed authenticity of my experiences, I thought for a long time I knew how to explain the flowering literature scene, the success of so many Graz authors at the beginning of the sixties through to the end of the seventies, those who began to write and were published here for the first time in the magazine »manuskripte.« I held it to be the result of a calculated and heroic »escape from the province.« From the present perspective of time and space, this view loses its certainty. Today I can hardly remember the absurd details of the conflict round artistic modernism, or the small town quarrels between conservative cultural administrators and communicators on the one hand and the avant-garde artists on the other, offering provocation, storming conventions. It is disconcerting when I read the documents.

One thing that has remained alive in my memory from that time is my own ambivalence formed of engaged excitement and apathy. Basically I felt a strange indifference towards all cultural aspirations; many works of art, even avant-garde ones, did not interest me. I wanted to read and did so, but had no real scale of values because I didn't want to be considered a »cultured person.« Paradoxically, when the threshold of my repeatedly denied »culture,« and above all my literary interests, was impugned by teachers, officials or people active in public life, I reacted with angry hostility, defiant provocation and demonstratively inappropriate behaviour to all impositions of the »traditionalist.« I shared this irritability with many pupils, students and cultural managers. Some of them did not want to accept the stupid, small-town narrowness which prevailed in Graz at the end of the fifties. They desired to have access at last to information about modernism in the first half of the twentieth century in order to link up with the historical and aesthetic knowledge and experience of a forgotten avantgarde. This need for »excitement,« the interest in the »new,« stood in contrast to the educational and cultural institutions that insisted on the conventions and traditions of a normative understanding of the arts.

The conditions for establishing a new modernism were propitious. At the end of the fifties and beginning of the sixties a structural change in the public took place to an extent previously unknown. The media became more pluralistic, the amount of medially available picture and text information grew in exponential steps in ever-shorter time spans. Mass mobility increased and general knowledge about the difference between real reality and reality as represented in human consciousness crept into the awareness of the time.

The »Graz authors« such as Alfred Kolleritsch, Barbara Frischmuth, Wolfgang Bauer, Gunter Falk, Peter Handke, Michael Scharang and later Helmut Eisendle, Gerhard Roth, Gert Jonke, Reinhard P. Gruber, Bernhard Hüttenegger, Alfred Paul Schmidt and many others who came along later and whose names are connected with Forum Stadtpark and the literary magazine »manuskripte,« belong to three generations. The first group are those born shortly before the Second World War and who experienced the final phase of the dissolution of a social order in their childhood, the establishment of a totalitarian state, the catastrophic collapse of that state during the war. They heard the sirens and saw the cities and villages destroyed by bombs, grew to adulthood at a time of hope and renewal without being able to get rid of the trauma of destruction. The second generation were those born during the Second World War who, as small children, experienced the world in a condition of war. After the end of the destruction, in a time of hope of ethical renewal, they were cheated, little by little, of exactly that. The third group, born immediately after the war, traumatically aware of the signs of devastation, were forced to take care of themselves in the bustle of re-construction and they witnessed a cold (ideological) war whose mendacity poisoned many areas of public and private life.

What links these authors and the literature published in »manuskripte« in the first twenty years of the artists association Forum Stadtpark is neither style nor theme; method nor programme and not even the oft-invoked illusion of friendship. The basic pattern of a loss of trust in the world is the lowest common denominator of GRAZLITERATURE. Out of memories of horror, powerlessness, speechlessness, senselessness and immobility grew a desire to reconstruct the experience of the self and reality in a subjunctive structure outside of any normative commitment. It is a desire for a potential reality that can unfold in (linguistic) games without the things that are unambiguously named hitting back at the self. The juxtaposition and mutual influence of the various ways of thinking, conventions, life styles, and life experiences intensified so much in the sixties and seventies in a re-organised Europe that the individual was continually being called upon to take sides, provoked by some events and bored by yet others without ever having had the chance of discovering the inner logic of widely differing events and phenomena in the flood of information. An acceleration of action and reaction happened and following the laws of inertia, initially limited the individual's freedom of movement and then changed many details of it. With many people this produced a feeling of dropping out of reality, of being subjected to perceptual exclusion, threatened by delusory experiences and the dissolution of common values. Reality appeared on one hand as a crippling tangle of meanings and relationships and on the other as a stimulating, sensual chaos.

No-one has been able to provide a better explanation for the fact that this cultural history phenomenon had a not insignificant crystallisation point in GRAZ-LITERATURE and one is not needed.

THE LEGEND OF THE ORIGIN
OF SCHLOSSBERG

Once upon a time a long time ago a feast was held on the Schöckel. At it, the magnificent height of the mountain was praised. There was a stranger who made fun of the people and said that elsewhere there were mountains that were much higher than the Schockel. If they liked he, the stranger, would place a cone on the top of the mountain such that it would then be higher than, say, the Rigi in Switzerland. The only condition he stipulated was that whoever was the first to climb the built-up hill top belonged to him. As the devil revealed himself in this manner, people were greatly horrified. They were afraid. Only Bergsteffel, a well-known ruffian offered Satan his hand, and the contract was made.

The devil flew to Africa and there he ripped a huge piece of rock free and returned to Styria with it.

But as he was between Wildon and Graz, almost at his goal he saw a procession and remembered that it was Easter Sunday and that hell had no power over mankind. Angered greatly he shook himself free of his heavy burden and it fell with a terrific crash into the Mur valley breaking into two pieces and boring their way into the earth after the fall. They still lie there to this day. And that is, according to legend, how the Schlossberg and the Kalvarienberg were formed.

HUGO BLOTIUS

(1534–1608)

Schlossberg

Graez or Graccium is a city of middle size, well enough fortified and an archduke's seat which Archduke Karl fortified in part right well and in another part made resistant. From the north the Schlossberg rises steeply and it is surrounded on all sides with mountains so that it is particularly suited to be a fortress because of its cliffs. The part that faces towards the city slopes gradually downwards and is joined to the same. The castle occupies the entire saddle of this mountain which is well fortified from nature and the hand of man. It is both magnificent and goodly to look on. A double wall and massive fortifications protect it for the most part. On the summit of the mountain itself a very high and splendid castle towers up over the nicely painted and appointed walls. Inside there are four or five military barracks, some of which, on the ground level, are used for storing war rations and serve well enough for the defence of the armoury square. Against the north side of the Schlossberg lies a garden planted with vines and it is large enough to serve for deer and other animals such as cattle. There are no woods with the exception of a grove of oaks which in part stretches down to the river. Thus where the sun rises is the garden, around midday it is on the city and at sundown on the River Mur, towards the

north the vineyard, on the side of the Schlossberg
cliffs and boulders that have always been there tower
upwards.

RUDOLF HANS BARTSCH

(1873–1952)

The country throws open its windows

All around the Schlossberg the country is throwing
open its windows, it is too much to limit to a single
atmosphere. Threatening mountains, smiling hills,
darkly brewing clouds here and boiling hot sunshine
there. The watery meadows swim in silvery shimmering light, the south lies in a blue haze, there is more
than enough spilling out for everyone.

MAX MELL

(1882–1971)

The Bad Mistress

Smoke wisping its way peacefully over midday roofs.
Whoever looks down on the old town of Graz from the
Schlossberg, into the narrow spaces between the tiled
roofs, sees little bits of courtyard and window in

which the minor details of daily life are on show along with the bustle which gives it away just as the smoke does. He takes this picture away with him with pleasure. I once talked to someone who knew how to look at things like an artist and was happy to have retained this view above all others. It appeared to me that the glimpse that the old woman gave me into the life of the Styrian craftsman's house when she young was of that sort. She told me about her family, about things that were the pride of the house or that gave her pleasure and those things that stood around her flat helped her to tell it. They even talked to the visitor who had just entered and they asserted their own peculiar life in an unusual way. There was a grandfather clock in the first room which made a point of forcing the attention of those entering on it. Above the clock face, on it's case, just above the height of a man, there was a cut-out triangle. Every time the pendulum swung that way, an eyeball could be seen at the opening and looking at you. The sides of the triangle were decorated with sunrays on the clock case because the eye was didactic: the eye of God sees you at all times. You can say what you like about the old fashioned taste of the piece but you couldn't avoid the hard gaze because it appeared continually. A little notice which was stuck on the inside intimated that it had been purchased in 1838. A heavy table with an egg-shaped top in the room next to it exhibited a similar testimonial. The old woman reached under the oak tabletop to where a paper envelope was glued to it. It contained the note on which stood the following in an old-style handwriting: »Vinzenz Vonihr, Locksmith of

Graz had this table made for his wife Aloysia on the 27th June 1813 for her name day for a price of 25 florins in redeemable notes.« The eighty-five year old niece of the locksmith led the conversation in a peculiar, Styrian mood and recounted how it began and how he succeeded. A hofrat* lived in that same house in Marschallgasse and a young maid, the daughter of a Carinthian doctor, came to visit him. Father Vonihr and son Joseph were looking out of the window and saw how deftly she moved around the kitchen. The father watched her going about her business for a while and then he turned to his son and said, »I like the look of her. She's the one you should marry.« The son gave no answer. He had thought exactly the same but he couldn't have stood to be rejected by his father if he had said it. He was happy to be introduced to the girl and when he had won her heart he went to his father and told him he had taken his advice.

HÉLÈNE HALUSCHKA

(1892–1974)

Secret Magic

There is a rare kind of woman, and city, to whom you can swear undying love and never doubt the oath for a minute. You think you can just pass on by them with

---

* An honorary title given to senior civil servants in Austria.

a lightness of heart. They don't stand out, they don't display their attractions obviously, indeed, they hide them. They don't flash, dazzle and shout their joie de vivre from the rooftops. They are there, holding silent conversations with themselves that conjure a strange smiles to their lips. And the passer-by stops, captured by a secret aura … on a spring morning, on a sunny autumn afternoon, it could also be as a winter's day draws to a close, this meeting. It becomes an unexpected festival of minds, senses and hearts. These yearning travellers, seekers intoxicated with beauty, homeless, driven out of some parental home somewhere suddenly feel they have arrived. They've been re-admitted to something close to a human homeland that promises nothing but slowly grants everything that they ever wanted – human warmth, soul and beauty.

Graz is a city like that.

The city itself grown out of the green of its gardens round a wooded hill which impertinently (and for no reason) rises out of the surrounding plain: Schlossberg. Legend says that the devil lost the lump of earth and rock when he was carrying a mountain on his back. After so long, the exact circumstances are difficult to explain but one thing is certain, the Evil One most certainly stole the chunk here from the Garden of Eden.

Come and look for yourself. It is spring. On the slope laburnum, lilac, hawthorn and wild cherry are blooming. And look at the wonderful rockeries. On the cultivated terraces they offer up their flower beds like precious mosaics or colourful brocades. A splendour of saturated and luminous colours without compare. An avenue dense with blooming Japanese cherry trees will wave their pink clouds in the blue sky later in spring and then shake their petal rain down onto the red-brown earth. The breath of the wakening Schlossberg floats in the wind as intoxicating fragrances – the green astringency of the young leaves, the heady sweetness of the lilac, the confusing perfume of the jasmine, the aromatic freshness of the alpine flowers. Up there it is a spring of blooms and scents as if the world had just been born.

But perhaps it's autumn and the flames of the wild vine, the purple of the ash trees or the transparent gold of the birches are blazing, consumed in a dying more passionate that in life.

Is there an autumn like this anywhere else?

It is winter. Do you know that there are Graz lovers who come from far off to wait up there for this very hour? Twilight, that sinks with the dusk over the snow-covered roofs of the city …

FRANZ NABL

(1883–1974)

Castle Rock Tunnel I

The earthy rubble (produced by building the tunnel) brought into the light of day was dumped in the middle of the city forming tremendous heaps on top of the riverside walls of the Mur which were guarded by creepers.

When the awful piles of rubble were cleared away again later they had already partly choked the roots and tendrils of the creepers which had been planted. However, on the small strip between the base of the wall and the river it began to go green and sprout in a wonderful way ... a victorious invasion of the landscape in the middle of the city and thus a real symbol of its essential, ever-regenerating character ...

ALFRED KOLLERITSCH

(* 1931)

Castle Rock Tunnel II

As my brother and I ran out of the not yet reinforced tunnels during the heavy bombing attack on the 1st November 1944 and while bombs were still falling, we saw the destroyed dormitory block and the dust clouds above it. The mountain was a safe place compared with the destroyed building. The master in charge was a badly wounded officer and secondary school teacher who had treated us like dirt. The mountain remained the past, the world, the mid-point determining all directions of the compass both far and near.

GÜNTER EICHBERGER

(∗ 1959)

The Symbol

The most valuable find in a long time has been the symbol of Graz. It is the materialisation of a rainbow that once fell like a shooting star from the heavens, finding a resting place in the fissured cliffs of Castle Rock. When astro-archeologists dragged it into the light of day it had already assumed the characteristic black colour of a dead rainbow. It was welded onto the narcissus yellow lookout tower of the castle after which the mountain takes its name. Nowadays the symbol looks a little ragged like a dark piece of cheese. The legend is to blame for that, the one that ascribes it with healing powers for all kinds of suffering. It is no wonder that some of the infirm tried to break off a chunk or at least a crumb of it for themselves, something which happened again and again in spite of strict controls and heavy penalties. In the meantime the battered rainbow has been coated with a transparent, impenetrable protective layer in order to make further infringements impossible.

BERNHARD HÜTTENEGGER

The so-called Mountain

If, by chance, this so-called mountain had not grown in the middle of the city naturally, it is not unreasonable to assume that at the time the first settlement was built the people who founded the city would have left a generous space in the centre and each of the house-building settlers would have made a founding donation of several hundred dressed stones and have piled them up with bee-like diligence thus ensuring that the so-called elevation came into being anyway.

MECHTHILD CURTIUS

The Cerrini palace on Friday morning, 4th May 2001, 4 a.m.

Graz, in the Cerrini palace on Schlossberg, on Friday morning, 4th of May 2001, 4 o'clock. Down the mountain before dawn and dew and walked through the old town. Discovered something new, during the day throngs of people and no possibility of standing still to look up at the walls or to follow the shield-shaped monument plaques information. A lot of Renaissance, a lot of Baroque, internal courtyard with multi-tiered arcades, during the day all the squares are full of visitors, the alleys are thronged with passers-by who push those who stop into carrying on against their will. In the early morning I can look at the »only house in the City of Graz with a Gothic façade,« as it says on a plaque until a rubbish lorry chases me away with toots and rattles; Sporgasse is steep and narrow, the ground floor of this house being a »an award-winning Austrian confectionary shop.« One decorated oneself with superlatives, fluttering and flattering with titles and not only those from the university who are present at dawn today on some of the squares; action days »university for all« – young scientists are supposed to be demonstrating that their faculty earns the tax money it gets. Zoologists show their research results on hand-sized crickets whose acoustic signals are to be seen on monitors, geologists present different kinds of rock and their formation over millions of years and the River Mur behind their table carries many species of stone with in, a heap of them are lying at the side of the road, hazelnut, walnut and co-conut-sized pieces. They're called »Mur dumplings,« so that every stranger like me knows that any rounded form is called a dumpling. On request the geologists cut a veined stone with a screeching saw and inside is even more colourful and shines like the marble in a Florentine palace. The marble in the cathedral is similar in colour and form to the arabesques, reliefs and frescoes, putti tutti epoci of the high Gothic, Renaissance and Baroque, although the architectural history of Graz itself begins with Romance relics. In the mausoleum nearby, Grazer princes sleep the eternal sleep; in the crypt, in red marble and splendid costume are the Spanish grandees with corrugated wheel collars, the lovers Archduke Karl and Maria. From their stone sarcophagus they could see the circular eye of the window in the centre of the dome if the view was not blocked by the marble altar at which holy mass is celebrated over their heads. Thus they have become church relics and the rituals of Catholic heaven have forced themselves between the couple and the cloudy skies of the visible universe. School classes tiptoe around until a teachers explains motifs from Christianity and mythology to the nine year-olds. Tu felix Austria is already receiving a classical education in the primary school. A group of mentally handicapped children follows them, one of the youths has that kind of leather protection around his brow and brain just like those I experienced on people of the same age in my childhood in Bethel by Bielefeld. They were cleverly attentive. On a rise in the Teutoburger Woods I called desperately for my rust-red setter that had vanished into the bushes. They gathered round my and consoled me. »He'll be back.« I meet the Grazer children again on the Schlossberg. For pupils on both sides of the border it is obligatory to stand on the top of the Schlossberg at least once during your school years, as defender Lieutenant de Cerrini did long ago. And I go from the Cerrini Pavilion up the stone steps, close the gate that sticks, run through the rose bower and study how far the red and yellow buds have opened till I get to the view over Graz, passed the far-distant chain of mountains to the horizon. I trot first through the flower beds enclosed by box hedges in the Herberstein Garden on a snail-shell like path that winds down the Schlossberg and photograph at each level Grazer roofs, landscape panoramas and mountains which are clear today, obscured tomorrow. Pant upwards again, snap details, blooming roses and the bunched blue flowers of the wisteria, the upward jutting glass tower of the lift through the Schlossberg, the square clock tower and the three gardeners at work, I ask them a few questions, the head gardener, Ludwig, learned at Schloss Eggenberg, he says, Getrud learned agriculture at home with her parents, beans and pumpkins. Peter doesn't come from farming and gardening at all, he gave up working in gastronomy and is looking for a new start. This morning they weed out all the flowers, including those in bloom, and throw them into wheel barrows, gardener Gertrud drives a tractor which has tracks instead of wheels up the steps and lets me take things from the weeded out bunches. A bent old lady with bandaged legs hobbles up the mountain, calls and persuades, feeds the stray cats that are even worse off than she is. I don't dare to photograph her, but like all the early birds, we greet each other with a smile. She unpacks her sandwich, I return for breakfast with my painter-man in the little Cerrini palace, carefully going up the steps, the stone stairs are slippery with green caterpillar-shaped walnut-flower sausages, the crown of the nut tree spreads out over the stone trough in the courtyard next the stairway. The rusty memorial plaque between our window and the green door of the house makes brown rust marks on

the white wall and its inscription tells us that Baron
Karl von Cerrini built the little palace which is a pavilion in and on the mountainside.

GÜNTHER EICHBERGER

(∗ 1959)

The City of the Black Rainbow

A high concrete wall is supposed to protect the blot
on Graz, the slum area Geidorf, from the gaze of curious tourists. The poorest of the poor live in holes,
old people or invalid Jakominis, creatures with such
repellent deformities that their sheer repugnance
permits no pity. Babbling idiots continuously secret-
ing spit and mucus, ragged figures whose hereditary
profession of begging is forbidden & who consistently
resist every re-training; former criminals who no
longer have a foothold in their trade, brutally animal
wrestlers and weightlifters with sports-related brain
damage, emigrants, missionaries who spread reli-
gions other than that of the state, political refugees &
lepers. Epidemics rage through this place of hopelessness, no medical help is given because of fear of
infection. Despite plague & cholera, the completely
isolated ghetto which appears on no town map is
ineradicable. However, as those in the know imply, a
secret plan by the municipal authorities to rid the
Graz world of the problem of Geidorf has existed for

some considerable time. If you look down from Schlossberg onto the colourful, varied landscape of houses
you will be caught in a wave of familiarity, you feel
strangely at home. Some travellers cannot content
themselves with a short stay and become permanent
visitors, living & dying here. Could you say anything
nicer about the appeal of a city?

ANATOL GINELLI

(∗ 1927)

The gothic double spiral staircase

As witnesses for the prosecution I call on the master
builders Peter Parler and Ulrich von Ensingen; the
unknown master builder of Košice Cathedral in Slovakia;
the master of the Eferding Parrish Church in Upper
Austria and the Infirmary in Kirchberg am Walde in
Lower Austria, as well as Professor Friedrich Mielke,
master of the science of stairways and Architect and
Engineer Royal, Johann Berhard Fischer von Erlach.
In particular, Mielke draws attention to the fact that
a) that »Peter Parler's variation of the mono-central
spiral principle,« the staircase in the Veit Cathedral
in Prague (1372/1373) might be seen as the precursor to the Graz Stairway, and that this achievement
worked »as a stimulant« and could regarded as a con-
tinuation of the work that Parler began when, at the
end of the 14th century, Ulrich von Ensingen built

Ulmer Münster; b) the three Austrian twin spiral staircases, Eferding and Kirchberg have a late Medieval character and that Košice also »profited« from Parler's unusual construction in Prague and that c) the Collegial Church in Salzburg contains an imitation of the Grazer staircase and it is certain that other buildings of a later period such as the library of the Vorrau Monastery in Styria with its cast iron twin spiral (1730); Castle Molsberg around 1760 and even the Provincial and Administrative Court in Berlin in 1900 do as well.

AQUILINUS JULIUS CAESAR

(1720–1792)

Mur suburb

The name Mur suburb came from the river Mur and was given because at the time Graz was surrounded by a number of suburbs. It is now very great in extent and numbers 954, almost 1000 houses, although the city encircles within its walls only 404. It lies quite open, without walls, lines or gates ... In this century the suburbs have grown a great deal especially because of the barracks, hospitals, the workhouse for the poor, the prison ... there are 111 inns in the Mur suburb, 2 coffee houses and 954 other houses ...

REINHARD P. GRUBER

(∗ 1947)

The sausage stand

The sausage stand belongs on the Hauptplatz of Graz,
it's where young and old meet. The sausages are also
young and old. The young are the Frankfurters that
taste very good and have a very smooth skin and the
old are the Krainers that are wrinkled, fat and ugly,
unpleasant looking. When you bite into a Frankfrter
nothing happens. If you bite into a Krainer the grease
squirts onto your neighbour like it did with my grandma.
Because of that neighbours at the sausage stand always have on a Styrian costume that is a bit greasy.
The grease sticks to the collars particularly well, but
there you don't notice it anyway.

And while we eat and eat and drink a Fanta, the
Weikhard Clock strikes 12. Immediately afterwards
the clock on the City Hall strikes 12 again, but it can't
be twelve twice, right after another, I think, and wonder if in Graz it's maybe 12 o'clock the whole day
long! My granny doesn't have an answer to that either
and instead shows me a toy shop. Sadly it closes at
12. The stand owners on the main square don't care
about anything, they just wait until it strikes 6, but in
the evening. But they don't sell any of the vegetables
by 6 either. They'll bring them again next day and try
it yet again. There is so much there that our whole
family couldn't eat it. That's why there is always so

much left over on the main square. The stand owners have to eat what's left over themselves. Just look at them all, said my granny, they're all so big and fat. That's what happens if you eat too many vegetables and fruit.

KARL VON HOLTEI

(1798–1880)

Liebenau

There are October days so beautiful that they make up for a cold wet summer. It was on one of those days that I arrived in Libenau, not without effort since my hired coachman took the wrong road at least ten times after we had left the main road. These wanderings filled me with bliss. Thank god, I though, at last a place where no highroad runs and there is no railway. A place you have to look for, surrounded by woods where real, natural trees grow that you can talk to, as you do with trees of age and experience.

DORA LAUFFER

(1907–2000)

Protestant Bride – Catholic Groom

The bride affirms that for her part there will certainly be no marital problems arising out of the differences of belief. This is what the groom thought too and no more was said about it. The wedding took place according to Catholic rites in the Grazer City Parish Church. It was followed by a ceremony in the Protestant church on …. Kaiser Josef Square. The groom's mother refused to take part in it under any circumstances. Everyone understood. Guests were invited to a reception held in the hotel »Zur goldenen Birne.« Where was the mother, she had promised to be there at the right time. The guests covered embarrassment with conversation. The owner of the hotel looked in questioningly because the wedding breakfast was »burning.« In this disturbing and unexpected situation the groom, a military man, remained calm and relaxed. At last came the calls there is the dear lady, but in what a condition. Completely exhausted, silk dress torn, bleeding knee. My God, has she been run over? She shook her head continuously, she was patched up quickly.

In the end the reason for the injury is explained. The mother has crawled the 100 steps up to the Mariatrost Pilgimage Church fervently praying that her son would be forgiven his sin of marrying a heretic.

ALEXANDER RODA RODA

(1872–1945)

In Graz Cemetery

In the graveyard near Graz, behind iron grille
lie Theresian knights immobile and still
Major, Colonel, General and subaltern,
thoroughly mixed by death's peremtory call
grey pensioners, their rest they did earn –
Radetsky's battle companion, Haudegen,
famed through the army as a lout,
wise men, gaiter-buttoned scouts,
strategists, brawlers, veterans:
a single row of stout-hearted Croatians
Maroicic, Rodic, Grivisic.

Tombs inscribed with golden letters,
lions with ruffles, weapons and crowns
marble cannons with stony rounds,
the ivy grows from chiselled niches
geraniums, roses and anemones
with weeds in between.

If, at the Capuchins one day
Franz Joseph deigns to wake
and comes here to his loyal men
riding his silken brown Irish mare
and calls, in the ringing tones of grim command,
for a roll-call of his rotting horde:
My God, how the dreaded voice
would freeze the sleeper's bones!

He was so controlled in tone and gesture:
on duty – on duty he could get nasty.

That will be a huffing and puffing,
a running here and there,
until the jumbled heap
stand at ease in proper order.
A soldier may die when he will
but to receive top brass must conform to drill
according to rank.

On the right flank, the Field Marshals,
in the order of gazetting lists.
Then come the Generals,
the Quartermasters General in third place.
The Emperor will give them all a pinch.
»Field Marshall, are you fast asleep,
instead of working like a slave?«
The Marshall does but tremble and stutter:
»Your Majesty, you may roar with verve,
I know not who we're supposed to serve.
Old Austria with it's style and fame,
is no more except in name!«
And that old Franz the Emperor
would designate as shame.

My mother rests in Graz as well
to the right of Bonifaz of Lüben, Capt.
on her left is Hussar Major Schreiner,
who was always so amusing,
and opposite a Colonel of the Infantry.
So over there my mother has for her delight
a gentlemanly whilst party.

PAUL ANTON KELLER

(1907–1976)

Rag Market* I

Take pity on those who have never seen these Styrian
market days. Anyone who has experienced them often, seen them unfold in their rustic cheerfulness, will
never lose the memory. How the colourful currents of
people swirl and eddy, flooding past the market stands
and spreading out. City people and those from the
country, laughing, haggling, scolding, how the masses
back up because there's a tiny Punch and Judy theatre on a street corner which has become close to the
hearts of a dozen children, while immediately next to
that a butcher's wife with a rusty voice offers sausages. Their aroma mixes in a friendly-antagonistic
way with that of the candyfloss being made close by.
Ah, this belongs to one of the few carefree islands in
the dark dense undergrowth of the senses. The market stand owners, however, were more or less reduced
to being extras in the rag market comedy. The day
belonged to the people, and what the people were revealed itself in a strangely multi-facetted jumble offered from the world of goods. Beside the trash, kitsch
and jumble lies quality, unrecognised – shoes, dresses,
books, pictures, old iron and it lures the hunters from

---

* Originally the rag markets were concerned with textiles, new and
old. The term is now used in Styria as a general one for all kinds
of flea market, jumble sale, boot sale etc.

the horde of connoisseurs and no-one went home disappointed. The days of the Graz Rag Market blessed, retrospectively coloured in red on the calendar – you are one of the last places of pleasure since our childhood!

FRANZ NABL

(1883–1974)

Rag Market II

The river cuts the city in two in an almost straight line north south. Year in, year out it hurries on with its cloudy, sullen, brown waves, an unfriendly sight between the green bushes and it is almost impossible to imagine that it was once clear mountain water with the most noble fish, trout, grayling and huchen feeling comfortable in its waters. However, four times a year on the right bank, an event special to Graz takes place. The Mittfastenmarkt on the Friday and Saturday after Mittfasten (at the end of March), the Portiunkulamarkt on the 1st and 2nd of August, the Ägydimarkt on the 1st and 2nd September and the Andrämarkt on the 30th of November and 1st of December. The people called them »rag markets« and this somewhat derogatory name which is so evocative for all Grazer nevertheless, has persisted up to the present day. Some derive the right from privileges dating back to the middle of the 15th century and already exhibited a colourful, strange bustle decades ago. Certainly there were professional market travellers who in earlier times offered cheap, mass-produced goods for sale and offloaded them on the visitors streaming by, most of them farmers and country folk. But what was special was not the normal stalls. Anyone could put the things they had collected in their box-room or attic – useless rubbish, old crockery, rusted iron parts or tools, yes, even books and picture frames on the many tables or even on simple pieces of cloth spread on the ground, offering them in order to earn perhaps a few pennies before the things in question were finally consigned to the fire or the rubbish collectors. And it was exactly these things that lured on those with a treasure hunting instinct. They didn't look at the mass-produced goods at the dealer stalls but here they explored tirelessly. Sometimes they were successful in finding a beautiful old glass, a valuable and rare edition of a book or something else special from bygone ages and, paying very little for it, took it home with them with a feeling of bliss.

RUDOLF STIBILL

(1924–1995)

Kalvarienberg[*]

Wouldn't we, wouldn't we
be better off if we took
the Kalvarienberg
and flattened it
and built a high-rise on it
with a cross on top ...
And a newscaster with
running words advertising
a modern death,
more conscious of consuming,
day and night?

This old middle-of-the-road thing
between a carnival-show-booth passion
and sudden, still piety,
tilting walls,
brittle old stairs,
it is an annoyance.
Baroque spite protected
the devil's rock as a citadel
and no Napoleon
in a painted house
ordered it to be blown up.
So it stands there,

---

[*] Mount of Calvary

a religious carousel,
on which no child wants to ride,
stands there, and roundabout
a part of this city has grown up so strangely
that this cross can already
be viewed from above.

ALOIS HERGOUTH

(1925–2002)

A cheerful park

That's what the sun was able to do –
not only the flowers and the young people,
the newly fresh park is spilling over with gaiety. –
Fountains spray
cool silver on the grass
and squirt foam
into sky blue and leaves.
The huge mouth of a fish, that gulps the blessings,
glows and shines with eagerness.

All the paths are blocked as if there was a fashion show
No free space on any bench,
no small place on an ornate ledge.
Squirrels bravely frolic between stiletto heels
and the sparrows are clearly having fun
watching the parade
from down below.

And so it is that some smooth knee
encourages a little bravery and indiscreetly
is garlanded, pink on white, with dainty lace.
A warming wind
blows from the summer dresses
and here and there
a jacket turns, heedlessly.

A mouth, like cherry blossom – blond hair on
                                          turquoise,
a smile, brown and purest silk –
a strange, a well-aimed bolt of black ...
Eros makes music to surfeit
on his portable gramophone –
he laughs and chatters and speculates
and puts his money on today.

JULIAN SCHUTTING

(∗ 1937)

Schloss Eggenberg

Graz. Swallows, held fast in the fresco-blue sky flying around the pavilion and simultaneously in a sky
of the same blue. Schloss Eggenberg has 365 windows – a year of waxing, a year of waning advent?
From the planet room (it doesn't look like a plan-
etarium in the slightest, no dome in which the planets float, but the ceiling is covered by allegories

named after the planets). During a Chopin prelude (the lid of the piano is propped open like glasshouse windows during the day but it remains hot and humid all the same) looking out into the trees of the stately house park and into the darkening sky of the stately house park hoping for a breath of fresh air. What takes away your resistance to the warmth of candles in the middle of this closely-seated summer social evening, to the all-too-present Baroque flesh and the sultriness of thundery weather and smell of hay wafting through the windows, other than the melancholy of Chopin. Surrounded by candelabras, it causes the pianist in his evening clothes to perspire even more. Attracted by Chopin, the calls of the peacocks in the park, in contrast to the cries of love-filled cats, do not melt the stones but petrify them. You already know what should be done so that the windows might stay open and the room not heated more than it is at present – from each window a candelabra should be thrown at the peacocks, still burning, so that they run to the deer with their plumage singed. So, in the future, instead of shrilly screaming into the concerts they will accompany them with their weight-lifting ballets, fanning the air with their left-over twigs.

ANATOL E. BACONSKY

(1925–1977)

Mehlplatz

In my opinion Mehlplatz is the most beautiful square in Graz. If a carillon were to sound in the neighbourhood around here it would have to be the Magic Flute which once an hour improvised on Mozart's bitterly effusive melody. Mehlpaltz is also the most Styrian square in the city. With its very concise atmosphere it unites the fantastic, slightly cramped morphology of the German soul with Italian harmonies. It is a marriage the unique Gothic spiral staircase does not talk about. There, every breath of the south evaporates. There you have the feeling of entering a palace which has not been built by virtue of a human need to reorganise matter and subject it to principles of harmony but of being in a building of dreams where mounting the spiral staircase amounts to nothing less than an initiation ceremony. The alter ego climbs, strange, unsettling, on the other half of the stairway, continually merging with it simply just to separate from it again immediately. The aged stone is like petrified wood. Even the spiral form of the banisters appears to be a tree trunk wound around itself from an earlier, no longer verifiable exorcism. But this spirit is not totally foreign to me. My homeland, like all the other Latin countries is only half Latin. The other half comes from a mythology from the woods that came to us ...

WOLFGANG BAUER

(∗ 1941)

That was »Haring's«

Let's turn now to »Haring's« in Graz. It was never kitschy. It was dim, empty, full, penetrating, loud, drunken, enveloped in clouds of hot grog, overcast by the smoke of many of the world's tobacco products, spiced with »pepperoni,« made mild with »Calmus,« intellectual with intellectuals, picturesque and dramatic because of its leading actors, the artists, brutal because of the tattooed or blethering in a friendly sort of way by virtue of the elderly civil servants who often came in at six in the morning to fortify themselves for the coming workday. Haring's was a city in the city. The mayor was usually some lunatic and the political situation changed from one second to another, just as gestures of peace alternated with declarations of war, in thought, word and deed. Except for the morning, Haring's was not a »comfy spot« to be. Although the many little barrels with their ornate decoration exuded a certain charm, the spirit that resided in them was restless. As soon as you opened the door you walked onto some sort of stage with slippery boards, that signify the whole world here. You were never left alone because there was always an almost Shakespearian bustle going on. There was pushing and pulling, shouting, swearing and constantly some lunatic would stage a farce and over there someone was singing an aria and at the back, in the »poet's corner,« the level of sound was so great that a heavy metal band would have been green with envy.

Haring's was always an adventure, sometimes an annoying one, but it was never boring. Better that any film and much better than any theatre.

You were audience and leading actor at the same time. The creative and the compulsive blended into a volcanic cocktail. A sensation just had to happen every second; every sentence was composed and aimed. You were living by different rules.

Perhaps some kind of aliens were up to no good, I don't know.

»Haring Willie« only spoke in rhymes that were so confused and at the same time so deep that I had to immortalise him in »Gespenster.«

Veit Relin, who played his role, sometimes sat with him of an evening until the Haring role was almost identical with the stage role. Yes, now pictures of the guests: Gunter Falk developed utopias as did Oswald Wiener and Hans Pögl. Their theories were so daring they made you dizzy and they were not written down, disappearing into the vault that was Haring's. Artmann ordered »a schnapps all round,« Herwig von Kreutz- bruck held a mass, Othmar Kren fluttered around as a bull, Charly Haysen and Wolfhart Krainer smile (supported by their walking sticks), Achternbusch does a sommersault, Innerhofer gets angry, Eich- berger ponders, Wolf Wondratschek and Hubert Fichte: two stoic dandies, Georg Janosky holds a lecture, Kolleritsch accepts apologies from Falk, Martin Sperr is sobered-up with a soda-water shower, Attersee embraces Kurt Kalb, Fischerauer, Grilj and Bauer found the Lord Jim Lodge, Kippenberger and Oehlen design the seal for it, Guido Wieland stands in front of the camera with Towje Kleiner, John McEnrow takes a break from shooting, Hermann Treusch fights his gastritis with calmus, Main Square Kurti ambushes a female reporter, Waldorf punches some kidneys, Bisinger writes a poem, Kulterer distributes his »Eröffnungen,« Max Milo and Marin Petko intone a scream-opera, Ernst Jandl laughs monotonously to himself. Jörg Schlick knows what's going on in the cultural sphere, Rolf Dieter Brinkmann gets heated about the badly behaved public in Forum Stadtpark, Claus Schönerer dozes behind his quadruple gin, Falk only orders beer in tens anymore, the decimal system suddenly effective, and back there, good old Allan Ginsberg is drumming and singing and smiles at the young boys, in between there are often excitingly beautiful women who are magically drawn to this cave because this is where it's at, where it's all happening, here's where Eugene Ionescu fell in love with the old woman's dachshund and carried it out onto Mehlplatz where the snow was falling heavily, kneeled down with the dog, held it like an offering in the direction of the »Urania« and pronounced the memorable words, »Venice, Stockholm and Graz!«

The Haring is not a pub like any other. A place with a history has become a historical place. That's completely all right.

GUNTER FALK

(1942–1983)

The way to the lucky star

In a quarter of the city commonly known as the Triester
Estate – perhaps because it lay south-southwest on
the map without, however, being traversed by Triester-
strasse, the road which showed the general direction
to the aforementioned port city – in this quarter he
alighted from the public vehicle again without wast-
ing any thought at all on the nationality of his long lost
father but not without nodding more or less encour-
agingly at the driver. The latter acknowledged this
with a more or less astonished look. With his head
bowed (which was made possible by a certain con-
figuration of his skeletal musculature) and a dribbling
step (which had little to do with football and much
more to do with the state of his vegetative system) he
glided over the pavement. As he noticed the sign
»The Lucky Star« on a house in Herrgottwiesgasse,
Franz's nervous system slowed the frequency of his
stride almost to a standstill in order to give intention
time to ripen.

He entered the place. The door swung, his arms
swung back and forth, the smoke in the pub swirled
in garlands and Franz tramped heartily up to the bar.
He found a place for himself near to a gaming machine and his organism came to rest, apparently. His
heartbeat flutter ebbed, the skin of his brow tightened
up so the wrinkles disappeared and the muscle tone

of his arms sought a new equilibrium. He breathed and his smile was easily suppressed.

Franz sat, therefore, in the Lucky Star and suddenly thought he felt a stabbing pain in his heart. It was early in the morning, a thought took him unawares, and I'm drinking here. Franz had positioned a pint of beer in front of him, it stood upright in the middle of the table and appeared to be reasonably balanced – the surface of the beer only sloshed around a little (like a rapidly fading memory), the after-effect the publican's rough handling when planting the pint in front of Franz. Franz could clearly remember the act and its connections only when he cast his mind back. He had called to the only other man (apart from himself) inhabiting the pub because he wanted to drink here – he was dying of thirst and his heart was ready to burst. The beer bringer, with this ascription easily identified as the publican, carried out the prescribed actions with a quiet certitude, operated the buttons, taps and casks in the requisite order necessary to produce a beer. With a meaningful movement of his hand which in all probability he had inherited from his progenitors, he interrupted the golden flow at the right time otherwise it might, perhaps, have continued to flow forever. Franz tried to stare steadfastly at the publican, he remembers easily and at anytime. It appeared he could almost forget the pain in his heart, a pain which would certainly turn out to be psychological in nature and he glued his gaze on the unknown publican. He, on the other hand, by virtue of the stranger's orders – Franz's name was as unknown to him as his face – was not shaken in the slightest in his prognosticatory certainty and knew precisely the number of steps to make in order to fulfil the predicted outcome. At the same time the order was carried out and from now on Franz would be able to enjoy his beer. It was clear to him that all of this was indeed the case, he had observed the publican with precision, had absorbed enough of the reflected rays through his lenses over a period of time in order to achieve the necessary visual constancy. He brought me my beer, he thought, and now I can really drink it, his heart yearned for it. Orders, prophesies or their fulfilment did not occur to him. His sensual perception also remained closed to things like that. Franz calls out and the publican, also the stranger, brings it. The fact that you can depend on publicans is a secret of social reality. Franz was well-versed in reality, not just in social reality; he had lived in it long enough to know the appropriate methods and to be immune to surprises. Franz was forty-three years old, and all the years he had lived though had left traces behind. He could remember a lot about these years, his years or, as he sometimes said, his best years. He often liked to sit with a beer and think about it, let the years pass in review before him. His heart often hurt him when he thought of a past which he considered irretrievably lost. Then he would take a sad sip. He said cheers to the publican and took a sip, but the publican had already turned away and Franz remembered that it was still early morning. He looked at his watch and became aware that he was on the trail of truth …

KARL KRAUS

(1824–1936)

Captain Prasch

Captain Prasch is standing in front of his cover completely covered in blood, he holds a head above his head, stuck on a stick.

He says:

This is my first Italian prisoner, I did it with my own sabre. Before that I had my first Russian prisoner tortured. I like to go for the Czechs best of all. I'm a Grazer by birth. I cut down anyone I met in Serbia on the spot. I've killed twenty people, civilians and prisoners, with my own hands and I've had at least a hundred and fifty shot. Every soldier whowas tardy on the attack or who hid during the barrage I cut down with my own hands. I have always struck my subordinates in the face, either with a stick or with my fist. However, I have also done a lot for them. I raped a Serbian girl in Serbia and then left her to the soldiers. I had her and her mother hung from a bridge the next day. The rope broke and the girl fell in the water still alive. I drew my revolver and shot at the girl until she disappeared, dead, under the water. I always did my duty until the final breath of man and horse. I was decorated and promoted. I was always on alert. The war requires a tight bundling of all efforts. One cannot allow courage to diminish. Chin up!

GIORGIO VOGHERA

(1908–1999)

The »Jew«

When, in the spring of 1915, it had become obvious
that Italy would enter the war, father was of the opinion that we would be in great danger in Trieste. He
wanted to send mother and I to certain relatives who
lived in Livorno(Leghorn). He, on the other hand, as
a teacher in a state school, stayed in Trieste intending to join us later, perhaps via Switzerland. Then
Italy entered the war and we remained separated. All
of father's attempts to leave Austria failed; the war
dragged on longer than anyone had expected and
mother's state of health – she was just recuperating
from a severe illness – gave grounds for concern. So
it was us, mother and I, who returned to Austria through
Switzerland, accompanied by my grandmother (on my
father's side) who had fled first to Livorno. Our journey had its fateful events and it was interrupted by
long stays in one place. Although I have retained
many memories of it, I would still not say they impressed me particularly deeply. It was only after a
year of travelling that we settled in a little house on
Rosenberg, near to Graz, and my life again began to
run a normal course. We were not the only tenants of
the house which was surrounded by fields and had a
small garden. There were only a few children in the
neighbourhood, so I didn't have the numerous and
colourful company I was used to from Trieste.

I was much too different from the others in my clothing, behaviour and the way I talked that my comrades
could refrain from occasionally teasing me right from
the start, feeling justified in their superior numbers
…

…There were too many other things about me,
(even apart from my clothing and behaviour) that just
had to provoke my new schoolmates. I was a city boy,
they were all farmers; I was an Italian, a matter of no
small import. Then there was the problem of the two
surnames. That stimulated their curiosity (I did not
hestitate to explain to those who asked, without dis-
simulating or hiding anything). Finally there was also
the fact that I – a pupil of the third year – had slipped
into older forms and the teachers, ignoring that, often gave me difficult questions. Keeping all of this in
mind, I was extremely aware that difficulties could
not fail to materialise in the new school. However, my
astonishment was great when I found that the bad
feeling against me was aroused by another peculiarity, that had not caused any trouble till then. I was
»*the Jew*« in the class and that counted most; it appeared that in the eyes of my schoolmates this made
all the other »vices« natural. You can expect anything
from a Jew. The rest was forgotten; this was the point
to which they always returned, that was the one on
which they let out all their displeasure. What they did
to me could no longer be said to be pranks or little
acts of maliciousness. I felt surrounded by real and
genuine hostility. If there had been a little less dis-
cipline in the school, if the teachers had commanded
a little less respect, if the standard of what was al-

lowed and what not less strongly anchored in these
heads, then I would certainly have had to be prepared
for much more serious molestations and perhaps even
worse than that. They didn't do more than they did
because they knew the teachers would punish them
but they did take every opportunity to demonstrate
their hostility to me.

ARTHUR SCHNITZLER

(1862–1931)

Then the worms of Vienna will be happy

How long am I going sit here, then? It must be after
midnight …didn't I hear it chime earlier? What is
that … a coach driving past? At this time of night?
Rubber tyres – I might have known … They're better
off than I am – maybe it's Ballert with Bertha … Why
should it be Ballert of all people? – Just drive up! –
His Majesty had a nice little one in Przemsyl … he
always drove down into town with it to see Rosenberg
… His Majesty was very affable – a real comrade, on
first name terms with everyone … It was a really nice
time … although … it was a miserable region and in
summer you just languished … three taken with sun-
stroke in one afternoon … the corporal from my platoon as well – a very useful person … In the afternoons we lay naked on the bed. Once Wiesner came
in suddenly, I must have been dreaming just then and

I stand up and draw the sabre lying beside me ... that must have looked good ... Wiesner almost laughed himself to death – he's a captain already ... – Shame I didn't go to the cavalry ... but the old man didn't want that – that game would have been too expensive – but that's all the same now ... Why? – Yes, I know, I have to die, that's why it's all the same – I have to die ... But how? – Look Gustl, you *did* come down here to the Prater specially, in the middle of the night, where nobody can interrupt you – now you can think about everything quietly ... All that about America and resigning is just nonsense and you are just much too stupid to be able to start something else – even if you would live to be a hundred, and you think about someone who wanted to break your sabre and who called you a stupid boy and you just stood there and couldn't do anything – no, there is nothing to think about – what has happened has happened – and that with mother and Clara is nonsense too – they'll get over the pain – you can get over anything ... Look how mother wailed when your brother died – and four weeks later she hardly ever thought about it any more ... first she went to the cemetery every week, then every month – and now only on the anniversary of his death – the day I die is tomorrow – the fifth of April – I wonder if they'll take me back to Graz? Ha, ha! The worms in Graz will be pleased! – But that has nothing to do with me – someone else will have to rack his brains about that ... So, what does concern me? ... Yes, the hundred and sixty guilders for Ballert – that's all – apart from that I don't need to make any other dispositions – Write letters? What for? To whom? ... To say farewell? Well, what the devil, that's clear

276

enough if you shoot yourself to death – The others will
certainly notice that you've taken your leave of them
… If people only knew how indifferent the whole
story is to me, then they wouldn't be sorry for me at
all – it's not really a shame … And what did I have
from life? – There is something I would like to have
taken part in – a war – but I would have had to wait
a long time for that … and I know everything else …
Whether a person is called Steffi or Kunigunde, makes
no difference – and I also know the best operettas –
and I was at Lohengrin twelve times – and this evening
I was even at an oratorio – and a master baker called
me a stupid boy – by my soul, that's enough – And I'm
not curious any more – So let's go home, slowly, very
slowly … I really am not in any hurry. – I'll just rest
a few more minutes here in Prater, on a bench –
homeless. – I won't go to bed ever again – I've got
enough time to have a proper sleep. – – Ah! the air!
– That's something I'll miss …

ITALO SVEVO

(1861–1928)

When she appeared at the window the text disappeared in front of my eyes

My absentmindedness! That hinders my studies as
well. When I was preparing for my first national examination in Graz I carefully noted down everything

I needed for the last of these examinations. What happened? Shortly before the first examination I suddenly realised that I had learned things which would only be relevant many years later. So I couldn't take the examination at all. Naturally, I had only learned the other things cursorily. A girl from the neighbourhood was to blame for that. By the way, she had only flirted cheekily with me without allowing me more than that. As soon as she appeared at the window the text disappeared before my eyes. What a donkey I was to lose myself in such things! Even today I still see her small white face clearly in the window opposite, oval, framed by soft, red curls. I looked at her and felt that I had to lay that white and that red-gold on my pillow.

Mr. Äskulap growled: »Flirting is just normal and healthy. At my age you won't flirt anymore.«

Today I know that he didn't know what the concept of »flirting« was at all. I am now fifty-seven and say with certainty that even on my death bed I would throw looks of desire in the direction of my nurse if she was not my wife and my wife allowed me a halfway decent looking nurse! Or I would have to be cured by psychoanalysis. Or I would have to have given up smoking.

CLAUDIO MAGRIS

(∗ 1939)

Liebenau Penal Barracks

Cafés are also a kind of hospice for the impoverished at heart and café owners, like Lovrinovich, who offer temporary asylum from the rigours of life, are no less benefactors than the founders of a home for the homeless. And it is only right and proper that they should make money from it as well as possibly reaping fame throughout the land as Lovrinovich did after the San Marco had been destroyed and he had been imprisoned in the Austrian penal barracks in Liebenau near Graz where the Austrians incarcerated him because he had put glaucoma-inducing substances in both eyes so that he did not have become a soldier and fight against Italy.

IVO ANDRIĆ

(1892–1975)

Pupils and students from Wischegrad

Just as one warm summer night in August is the same as the next, the conversations of these students and pupils from Wischegrad were identical or very similar to each other.

One after another they arrived on the Kapija immediately after a hastily gulped evening meal, the day having being spent bathing and lying in the sun. Janko Stikowitsch, the son of a cloth cutter from Mejdan, had already studied natural sciences in Graz for four semesters. He was a skinny youth with a sharp profile and straight black hair. He was vain, sensitive, unhappy with himself but even more unhappy with his surroundings. He read a lot and wrote articles for Yugoslavian young people's revolutionary magazines which appeared in Prague and Zagreb. He wrote under a pseudonym which had already gained a degree of recognition. He also wrote poems and published them under another pseudonym. (...)

REINHOLD SCHNEIDER

(1902–1958)

The Triad

Ferdinand II wanted to be buried in Graz, and so he lies here in the mausoleum built by him.

... Mourning angels kneel in the dark. Silver vessels in a barred niche, dark as ore, preserve the dust of the rulers' hearts. Above on the altar of a side chapel there is a surprising motif in a baroque picture; death, buzzing down like a terrible insect terrifies the first humans. Above them shines the picture of the immaculate, the female saviour ...

The triad over the grave of the used up rulers' hearts, is the earthly crown of the City of Graz, a memorial of a time when it was the most important city in the south-east and on whose castle rock the Turkish hordes broke …

The city's greatest crown is something quite different –the long-established, baroque, decorated house in Stempfergasse is still standing. Here Johannes Kepler, teacher of mathematics and rhetoric at the provincial gymnasium Graz got married to the twice-widowed Barbara Müller von Mühlbeck. You can sit in the courtyard with a clear, strong wine till after midnight. Then the stairways and arches of the Kepler house come alive with returning occupants; the light comes and goes in the porches and galleries above the courtyard which is full of nooks and crannies. And now he could really stride by, the tall, serious man who failed to comprehend that people would not weep at the harmony of the heavens. He was a theologist and »was long fearful« till he realised that he could, as a theologist, do something he should have done long before – praise God as a thinking and cognitive being.

Following Plato's method, geometry proved to be a thing of God, to think it, pious. It was the century when the stars became fate: Giordano Bruno's fate and that of those who stood trembling before the silence of infinite space, Pascal, Wallenstein, Descartes and Galileo, the beaten witness. And it was from here in Graz that Kepler sent out his first cosmic message, the »Prodromus,« printed in Tübingen, a precursor,

a hint that goes before the sun and announces the
»Mysterium Cosmographicum.« From here he wrote
to Galileo in Padua to encourage him to fight for
Copernicus' truth. Galileo wrote back, happy but
somewhat taken aback by Kepler's theological and
speculative courage. The grandiose letter to his teacher
Mästlin in Tübingen is dated Graz, the 3rd of October
1595 ... Here Kepler develops the basic principles
of the harmony of the world based on his theology of
geometry and even if he still held to a circular orbit
for the planets, he indicated the last problem of modern physics. »Because light and movement are, according to their origins, certainly linked with each
other in effect, perhaps light is just the vehicle of
movement.«

WILHELM MUSTER

(1880–1994)

The twinkle in his eyes

... He always slept late and enjoyed it very much, he
almost never remembered dreams; what should he
dream, he who had almost everything when he was
awake and if he really did dream, something that only
happened when he slept alone once in a blue moon,
then a monstrous maypole appeared in front of him
for him to climb; hanging in the wreath high above,
between the fluttering ribbons, were bottles and salamis,

he would like to have had those very much, but the tree trunk had been greased with soap and no matter how high he pulled himself with his massive muscles he always slid back down and woke up sweating and cramped at which point he usually got up, passed water that pressed on his bladder, pulled the chain, sleepily listening to the rush of water and then went to the refrigerator, sliced off a huge piece of salami, drank half a bottle of beer just as if he had succeeded in climbing the maypole of his dreams, the meaning being child's play for any psychoanalyst to interpret, but he didn't think much of the eggheads as he called them, he was of the opinion that the eggheads shouldn't talk, a head was quite nice, but they lack something else all the more for that, and he understood that his interpretation of his dream was simple; while he slept afterwards he took a fancy to beer and salami so he woke up; this was by no mean unusual, he ate and drank with so much gusto that you could have said the activity was guzzling and boozing if it hadn't been so natural to him, so human; he ate what was put in front of him, delicately prepared roasts; he liked plain cooking best which is why he was wont to say, why should I scratch my head trying to find out what herbs and spices are in this dish or that, well, yes, that is marjoram, but that and that and that? why the Braunschweig (Brunswick) salami, it was common and therefore met his needs, so he ate almost everything; there were only a few things which turned his stomach, like a beef tartar, because, as he also said, am I supposed to eat raw meat, am I an animal? there again he was right, he wasn't an animal, he was a human being who made every housewife happy when they saw the twinkle in his eyes, even when they didn't know whether it was on their, the hostess's, account or related to the roast pork, which sat in front of him giving off an appetizing aroma, garnished with long-grain rice properly saturated in beef stock (it shouldn't be swimming, though, this rice from Italy or Spain) but J. wasn't just a well-loved, beloved guest, he was also a first-rate host who, from time to time, invited his friends, his women, to eat in one of the many good restaurants that existed in the city; what one ate where, what relationship price, service and size of portion had to each other; once, the »Steierhof« was to be highly recommended but then they started to shrink the portions excessively; I ask you, I go to a restaurant to eat not to meet high society there, it doesn't interest me, I know them all from other events, and here again he was right, and so he went to others, first to the »Wilden Mann,« for example, where you could talk in peace, you know where I mean, in Jakoministrasse, but there the portions were not quite right either, or he went to the »Steiermärkische,« the Stadt Keller, or to the railway station, always intending to give pleasure to the friends or women, feed them delicacies, it should be emphasized that although he didn't change his friends as often as his snow-white shirts, he did with his women, and when he thought about these women, if he ever thought about them in retrospect at all, it was not about how many times they had been in bed with him, but rather how many times they had eaten with him – wasn't all that screwing and thrusting, as I've said,

284

the most natural thing in the world – while eating was more refined, and so he seldom thought of the various beds, even when one collapsed once, but rather of the pubs and restaurants, even the dives, Mosser's for example, there you ate really well, also at the »Holzhof,« or the »Stern« in St. Peter's; in contrast, the Victorian Steakhouse, with all its fussy bits and pieces, was rather more suitable for young people who liked to see flames flaring while wrapped in each other's arms, their gazes never leaving the other and that, in turn, caused our hero to get an urge to laugh; he would have liked to say to them, quick, go on, go on! and if they also happened to be obsessed with meat, a first-class pepper steak, for example, the bloom of his flesh, to put it poetically, oh, my friends, how wonderful it is to be alive!

Once, on a Sunday, he sat in Pfeifer's, the place near the church in Maria Trost, high up on the hill, the pilgrims passing on their way to church, where, on the square in front of it the bought all sorts of things, models of the church that the devout could stick in their pockets, gingerbread hearts with clever, very often coded, sayings like »I will stay true 2 U 4 ever and ever« or devotional objects and pictures, candles, and then they went over to the pub, where J. was already sitting, he was not devout, but he liked to let the devout do what they had to do, and anyway they did it the same way as he did, and now the garden filled rapidly, the gravel crunched, chatter and laughter filled the happy air, the waitresses got a lot to do, children wailed or sat well-behaved on their chairs, the trees in the garden rustled with presentiment at the words that flowed through the reporter's pencil, anticipating the events now straining to be, but it would be best if it could come to a standstill, even if it was inopportune for the report, the sparrows hop backwards and forwards between the tables and J. ordered a meatball soup first, it was always first class at Pfeifer's, the chives floating on the greasy surface, J. spooned it up, enjoying it to the full, but he kept the pilgrims in view, or more accurately, the female pilgrims, since he was on the look-out, and he knew very well that even a devout disposition did not always reject earthly activity, J. exploited that, and slurping and spooning he peered around and he soon found what he took for something he could use, a girl of about seventeen summers, her breasts full and rounded in their bodice, a pretty, amusing face and spooning soup he immersed himself in the view of this rural beauty, who, for all her devoutness did not appear to have lost her sense of humour, and he ate and watched, as if he was lost in the depths of ideal beauty like a philosopher, because nothing stirred in him, no craving, and as he became aware of this, he put down his spoon, deeply shocked, and stared at her, but she turned away from him, blushing, and this, too, made no impression on him, and slowly it began to shudder, it made his flesh creep, it gave him goose pimples on his back, arms, legs, he felt that now it was a case of something more, now it was all or nothing.

What happened then is difficult to describe, and the author of these lines, who was not the friend of such

a remarkable and perfect man, but nevertheless knew
him well, otherwise he would not have dared to write
down this completely true story, sat beside J. on that
particular day, the one when he stared at the girl, and
she cast him sidelong glances, and you couldn't tell
if that was an invitation or if she wanted to know if she
was still going to be bothered by the gaze that she
perhaps regarded as shameless, but certainly not this
time, since J. stood up suddenly, tore the napkin from
his neck, took a few steps in the direction of the girl
and, what else is there to say, you could have sworn
that the clear day suddenly became dark, but that
would have been a bare-faced lie, so there really is
nothing more to be said, except that J. fell flat on his
face in the gravel, you could hear the screams of the
girls, from women, and as if on cue the church bells
began to ring loudly, they were still ringing out when
the ambulance came and transported the putative
death candidate to the local hospital. The soup remained unfinished.

J. didn't die then, he lived a long time, if you can call
how he lived living, in a bed in the psychiatric hospital, brimming with his flesh, sometimes he felt
worse, sometimes better, but he didn't speak much,
he occupied himself, most of the time, with an extended index finger drawing confused lines, which
no-one really knew how to interpret, a few of his
women came, most of them stayed away, as if they
knew what was waiting for them, a few friends and
acquaintances too; in any case the bed was surrounded
by flowers that had also been sent by anonymous peo-

ple, people who didn't want their names to be known; those that watched the tragedy, however, finally realised the meaning of the finger game, J. tried, now that he was helpless, now that he had nothing left, even his meals had to be fed into him, tried to remember previous desires and that seemed to be a very laborious business, he had women in all corners of the city, around a hundred or so, he didn't keep track of them and you might object that that was nothing, that there were others with five hundred and more on their trophy list, but you have to remember he was still young, right at the beginning of a dizzying career, that entitle him to the greatest hopes, women from Geidorf to Lend, from Jakomini as far as Gries, and if he had, like Kant, of whom he never learned, lived a life withdrawn from the world, he had, like the great philosopher, almost no experience outside of the city; but everything confused him now, as he tried to re-trace the streets and squares of his desire, he remembered dimly that behind that line there was a state of bliss, his whole life, he suspected it unspecifically, and so he travelled with his finger in the air, tirelessly, and when he was feeling a bit better, he hinted at it in a stammer, so that the visitor could make of it what he wanted to, now, because he lay dying perhaps, terrible Aphrodite ordered him around, when he, with trembling hand, waving around and couldn't remember anything anymore, only accidentally, and because he carried the topography of the places to eat and drink in Graz in his head, two line system soon were superimposed, became sticky, interfered significantly with each other, and the torture he suffered when, finally, he could do nothing with them anymore, and it paralysed his movements, cramped his hands, confused his eye, until everything confused him and the hand simply twitched on the bedcover, but still, the observer couldn't say that J. deteriorated terribly, it didn't happen so dramatically, but in his final night, when only an ancient holy sister took care of him, to calm the sudden nervousness, he felt for her hand, and cried or gurgled as well as he could, although she understood the sounds which came out of his spittle-foamed mouth, to be him calling for his mother, but the only witness to this was the night nurse, over-tired, and so, with certain reservations, you could say that the interpretation of the cry was arbitrary, maybe he didn't cry out at all, or the system of lines had become impossible to entangle or perhaps, at breakneck speed, had shrunk to a single point, that you could also have said, something was collapsing here as when a building suddenly caves in as if struck by the hand of a ghost, and this is what drew a cry or cries from his lips, but however it was, this final phase lasted a relatively short time, measured against time is measured by the living, then his breathing got shallower, and sometime during the early morning he just died away, the day he didn't live to see looked as if it would be nice, but rather hot. He didn't lie among the flowers for a lot longer.

JOSEPH ZODERER

(∗ 1935)

I never suffered from being a South Tyrolean in Graz

I spoke just like all the others. The different speech of mother and father was not conspicuous, it was like mother and father themselves – ordinary. I didn't notice anything. It was only after the war as father, lying on the kitchen sofa, talked more often of going home, of going into the land, that I remembered a side street to Herrengasse where I sometimes went with him into the Panopticum. Inside I sat in front of a thick black column and looked through a kind of binocular. This was how I became conscious of seeing the Tappeinerweg in Bozen for the first time. To be accurate, of seeing a holiday maker in a slouch hat decorated with artificial flowers wending her way down the steps of Tappeiner Promenade on her way to Gilf an der Passer. In doing so she had gathered her full-length pleated dress up a little. That was South Tyrol for me. That, and the empty shoeboxes which lay around on the pavement after the Bozen weekly market have remained in my memory. The red and yellow peach on the wooden railing of a bridge that I slipped unobtrusively into my pocket. The fountain in Untermais where my mother did the washing with my eldest sister. The woodpile in front of the house where we slept on the floor the night before we emigrated and a cat I had. Father was taken during the night; cries and crashing about and outside in the corridor he tussled with a drunken Haller, the prisoner. I saw father kneeling on Haller's chest and mother said —when he gets out again. The water of the Waal near the cemetery where I stood in my shirt-tails and mother sponged down my baggy breeches. Later I remembered more. I remembered when it was father's payday and Resi or I fetched him an anguilotto, an eel in oil and vinegar, in a coffee cup or a piece of gorgonzola. Papa was in a merry mood then – anguilotto, gorgonzola or mortadella. Otherwise, when he suddenly shouted, it didn't happen often, everybody collected in the kitchen. He would take the rest of the pile of terracotta plates from the kitchen cupboard and showed them around. Each of us knew – he's going to throw them onto the floor as well or, he won't throw them again.

As father lifted the pile up into the air I knew. Not today. He had grinned too early.

PETER DANIEL WOLFKIND

(∗ 1937)

Unsuccessful Elegy

Let's not write poetry. The Graz of today can no longer be captured in verse. The time of elegies has passed away. In today's world it's not possible to make an honest rhyme. Not even with Graz.

And you can't do much with nature either. On the one hand it has been thoroughly discussed. World literature is packed with sunsets going down behind mountains, golden window panes and shimmering rivers. The verbalization of the most intimate experience of nature has all been pre-fabricated by our poetic predecessors. The offer is enormous.

As far as nature is concerned, including nature in Graz, the fact is that it is getting less day by day. All right, all right, the sun. In all probability it will still go down behind the Plabutsch for some time yet. Even if the good old Mur gets dirtier or, and that's also a possibility, it might get a bit cleaner, it'll still stay liquid and have a smooth surface on which the sun can reflect.

But nature is being flattened. Covered in concrete and asphalt. Motors and machines have drowned out the lone violin long ago.

Foot by foot nature is being chased out of the city. Out of all cities. From Graz too.

But still, up there on Rosenberg, in Saumgasse, Bogengasse and in Charlottendorfgasse nature has found asylum. Some evenings you can stand there, close your eyes and believe that you're somewhere else.

Or you can open your eyes and look down on Graz. On Graz, a city just like every living city, remorselessly eating its way ever deeper into the landscape.

And if you find the wide panorama with its churches and high-rise houses, its smoke-belching chimneys, avenues, concrete streets, picturesque facades and nightmare blocks of flats beautiful in the yellow-hued

evening light; so beautiful you still think that you are
not in Graz but somewhere else, then the best thing
you can do is remain silent.

The beauty of Graz has lost its rhyme.

The elegy is unsuccessful.

PETER HANDKE

(∗ 1942)

The tried and true meeting places are also the right ones for learning

The places where one could mull things over as nowhere else sometimes became, during this years at
the university, places of evasion, comparable to movie
theatres; yet, while he tended to sneak into the latter,
he would enter his various jukebox cafes in a more
carefree manner, telling himself that these were proven
places for studying. This turned out to be a delusion,
for once he was alone again, for instance before bed-
time, and tried to review the material he had gone
over in such a public setting, as a rule he had not retained much. What he owed to those niches or hide-
outs during the cold years of his university studies
were experiences that he now, in the process of writing about them, could only characterize as »wonderful.« One evening in late winter he was sitting in one
of his trusty jukebox cafes, underlining a text all the
more heavily the less he was taking it in. This cafes
was in a rather untypical location for such places, at

the edge of the city park, and its glass display cases with the pastries and its marble-topped tables were also incongruous. The box was playing, but he was waiting as usual for the songs he had selected; only then was it right. Suddenly, after the pause between records, which, along with those noises – clicking, a whirring sound of searching back and forth through the belly of the device, snapping, swinging into place, a crackle before the first measure – constituted the essence of the jukebox, as it were, a kind of music came swelling out of the depths that made him experience, for the first time in his life, as later only in moments of love, what is technically referred to as »levitation«, and which he himself, more than a quarter of a century later, would call – what? »epiphany«? »ecstasy?« »fusing with the world«? Or thus: »That – this song, this sound – is now me: with these voices; these harmonies, I have become, as never before in life, who I am: as this song is, so am I, complete!«? (As usual there was an expression for it, but as usual it was not quite the same thing: »He became one with the music.«)

Without at first wanting to know the identity of the group whose voices, carried by the guitars, streamed forth singly, in counterpoint, and finally in unison – previously he had preferred soloists on jukeboxes – he was simply filled with amazement. In the following weeks, too, when he went to the place every day for hours, to sit surrounded by this big yet so frivolous sound that he let the other patrons offer him, he remained in a state of amazement devoid of name-curiosity. (Imperceptibly the music box had become the hub of the Park Café, where previously the most prominent sound had been the rattle of newspaper holders, and the only records that were played, over and over, were the two by that no-name group.) But then, when he discovered one day, during his now infrequent listening to the radio, what that choir of sassy angelic tongues was called, who, with their devil-may-care bellowing of »I Want to Hold Your Hand«, »Love me do«, »Roll Over, Beethoven«, lifted all the weight in the world from his shoulders, these became the first »non-serious« records he bought (subsequently he bought hardly any other kind), and then in the café with columns he was the one who kept pushing the same buttons for »I saw Her Standing There« (on the jukebox, of the course)

ALOIS HERGOUTH

(1925–2002)

The Garden at the Edge of the Gravel Pit

Mother is sitting on a stool. She is wearing a head-scarf, knotted under her chin like a farmer's wife. Her features are unclear but her eyes shine darkly and the thin shadows which run from her temples, over her cheeks to her mouth give an impression of its contours. It is the face of a country maid, humble and modest and you can feel the resigned obedience, poverty and early worries. Only her eyes are young. Above it is father's face, resting on a thick neck and strong shoulders. It is, however, sure and self-conscious, almost challenging. A Styrian hat sits slanted on his head, pushed slightly back so that the high, square forehead is bare. His eyes are set immediately under the brows. A bushy moustache with twirled ends sweeps up to the right and left of a mouth that seems to smile mockingly.

I only know father like this and from a few later pictures in which his face appears almost unchanged. He is always full of life, open-minded. My only real memory, though, is so far back I can no longer say what about it is reality and what invention.

It must have been shortly before he died, back then, when I was not quite four years old. I can see how he lifts me up on to his knee, laughing. Up there in the pub at the top end of the street. There are many voices present. It smells of rum and tea. He waves a pretzel in front of my eyes, laughs and shoves a crumbly piece of it into my mouth. Then I felt the scratchy moustache on my cheek. Somebody laughs too. Again that smell, movement and swirling threads of smoke behind which start to burn the eyes.

Mother was around me for another twenty years and my thoughts of her are indelibly stamped in my memory. I see her face in many different states – radiating happiness, serious or over-shadowed by a baffled melancholy but always that one thing, the only thing, the face of an old woman, a country maid who has grown old, tired from long service. Her hair was white before I came. I only know it like that, always getting lighter and purer until it radiated that blooming, untouchable shine as if it already shone from another world. Only her eyes always remained the same, here as there, present in their dark warmth and their distressing purity.

Both my mother and my father came from Lower Styria which belonged to Austria at the time. My mother came from the Slovenian south-east, from one of the cheerful vine-covered hills all around Boč, the subject of so many legends and which carried on far into Croatia. Father came from the edge of the plains south of Marburg. In both of them, their rustic origins were to remain determining the whole of their lives. He had trained to be a mason and worked in the villages and hamlets in the surrounding area. She was the daughter of a farmer, the youngest of seven children. The little thatched cottage on the side of a hill above Sladka gora near to Svet Mihel wasn't big enough for everyone and the sloping fields, meadows and vineyards did not produce enough to fill all the mouths. At fourteen she had to go into service with strangers, down on the richer land on the plains. There they met each other and it was from there that they followed the current of people who wanted to make new lives for themselves in the flourishing, much praised provincial capital. They were young and like many of the others they set off on foot taking little more than hope and the strength of their hands with them. Graz, a beautifully developed city, had work for all who wanted it. It also had bread and wine and enough space to build a home even if it wasn't any bigger than one down there in the hills.

We children who were born and grew up here loved it from the very beginning even if we never talked about it much. The street in which we played as children, the odd-cornered courtyards and the meadows and gardens of the suburbs were beautiful enough for us. It was here we discovered the small, wild world which was our home. We loved it with all the love one can have for a homeland. We knew no better and wanted no more. Here, too, we learned the language that mother spoke but brokenly to the end of her life and she spoke it with a soft, lilting accent. We often laughed at the twisted words that resulted – ›braveyard‹ (graveyard) or ›lezgo shursh‹ (let's go to church) – but more about the way the people spoke who paid a visit from Slovenia now and then. The aunts and lower Styrian uncles and ›lower Styrian cousins‹ who could not pronounce one single syllable correctly. Though it's certainly true that we heard speech like that in the tenement house and on the streets as well sometimes. From that and what we learned in school, we mixed our own dialect.

It annoyed us the people called the Moserhofgasse, the street where we lived the »Windische Herrengasse.«[*] God knows who started that ...

---

[*] Windisch Men Street. Windisch is a Austo-Bavarian pronunciation of the German Wendisch, Slavic. The word Slovenian did not become prevalent until the middle of the 19th century. Windisch was retained in colloquial German by the Slovenes of Carinthia and Lower Styria.

... Our flat was small but light. At the time is lay a little way off from the mass of the houses and towers out of which the Schlossberg rose and was separated by a green area, as green as the green of the south.

The city itself was and remained foreign for our mother, we knew that. She tried secretly but persistently and doggedly to keep us away from its hustle and bustle. I have no childhood recollection at all of the way to the nearby Münzgrabenkirche or about anywhere further than the long grey wall that could be seen in the north.

There are only the hidden places in courtyard and cellar, in the forbidden, neighbouring gardens, the path at dawn up over hill and meadow into one of the big woods in which there were blackberries, mushrooms and dry branches for winter. How many time I went that way, sometimes sullenly and sleepily but also full and soon to be saturated by the freshness of open country. I learned to love the greenery, the secret language of the grasses, leaves and flowers. Mother with her colourful headscarf, the small handcart scraping along, the songs of the birds among the leaves, the shimmering tree tops and the mossy tree roots in between which you could catch sight of mushrooms like the magic buildings of dwarves or fairies – those were the most beautiful colours and sounds of the time. The way to the cemetery was also familiar and lacking in mystery. It lay at the upper end of out street exactly opposite the inn. It was light and friendly above the graves, the whole summer long it

flowered there as if it was a garden and even in late
autumn there were nights in which innumerable lights
continued to glow in the thick fog above the cypresses
and spruces. Mother went up there very often, to pray
and to water the flowers and while I was small she
took me with her every time …

INGRAM HARTINGER

(∗ 1949)

Summer in Graz

Experiences during the last weeks allow me to write
these lines. Experiences I have had with myself and
two friends who stayed here in Graz over the summer.
My first summer in Graz, a cool summer, a summer
in a city in which one could completely disappear
without it ever being noticed. Forever. You could take
leave of yourself in another season, in a melancholy
poetic autumn for example, but it doesn't really depend on the external temperature as to when you do
»it« or why. So what does it depend on? Internal temperature? But that's nothing more than simply a psychological allusion. I say you can disappear without
anyone noticing. In this city here there is nothing
which can rescue you from a situation like that. Nothing. You can scream and no-one will hear you. There
are pubs and a few social centres where »King Alcohol« reigns. Read Jack London's socially critical

novel, »The Iron Heel« or »The People of the Abyss«. There you find an exact description of the situation. Or go to the Glockenspielkeller and read Gorky's »Night Asylum«. What does it depend on when you do »it« and why? End of August. A lot of people are on holiday now. Graz is emptying, people are leaving so that having attained sufficient regeneration of working energy they can come back at full power. It's not rumbling quite as much in Graz's huge, half-empty stomach. Lately the steaming and pulsing of the city is slightly apathetic. Doze, paralysis, headache, loneliness. I remember the demands David Cooper made to a local authority. There should be a place where you could scream your heart out, cry yourself dry. Where you can express your suffering at last. Where there are others to accompany you, to listen to your worries and LET YOU BE. A place where you can re-discover what you lack, what you need, and where you discover it along with others and actively fight for yourself and others to feel better.

No, there's nothing like that in Graz. And so it is that during the aforementioned summer months certain manifestations make their appearance, those our society needs for self-defence and for controlling of the »deviant majority«. They are our well-tried institutions of prison and psychiatric hospital. During these weeks the number of inmates grows.

M. lies in Feldhof now. I only found out about it a few days afterwards. An observant chemist discovered his intentions and dutifully reported it to the responsible expert. The ambulance appears, M stops resisting, the fight is over, »true, I've been heard by the wrong people, but that's better than not being heard at all.« The ambulance turns into Feldhof. »Why did you want to do it?« That was the question. There was no answer to it in those first few moments. M. had wanted to call me before it happened. I wasn't at home. Another friend had a similar experience. His sister called him from faraway Munich on the night of the aforementioned accident. She didn't get through to anyone. That night she did it. It doesn't matter why. She wanted to live.

Summer in Graz. Nobody at home. A few telephone numbers in my wallet. Rain will come in the next few days as sure as the taxi. H, the second friend, drove home in a taxi around three in the morning absolutely plastered. Wife and children had taken off. No wonder. Afraid of the last ecstasy and the fact that he assumes the right to express himself, to communicate in such a radical way. But it must go wrong, summer in Graz, there's no-one there.

»But look,« I said to him, »I'm here. Let's get out of this pub. I'll drive you home. We'll make ourselves something to eat ...«

Long after midnight, it was raining outside, we began to talk about the place where you could shout and cry. H. stared at the wall. He couldn't quite grasp what I meant. The neighbours were certainly asleep. You couldn't scream here, crying would be the most you could do, a quiet sobbing.

That's what H. did. He hid his head in his hands and was silent. Now it didn't matter what I meant. He was well on the way to expressing himself. He fought, and I wanted to be at his side.

A long time later he put on a record from »good old« Bob Dylan, a track that I like. All Along the Watchtower.

In my head I slowly and laboriously translate a key sentence: »There are many here among us who feel that life is but a joke.«

Attempted suicide is what it says on the referral certificate. The referral letter from the doctor begins: »To the laudable clinic«. Date: Summer in Graz. There's still nothing that can save you from a situation like that.

4th September 1977 (»Diary«)

WOLFGANG POLLANZ

(* 1954)

The Way the Women of Graz Walk

From the window of my basement flat I can see people out for their Sunday stroll. It is a mild May afternoon and from the city park nearby the twittering of the birds carries this far, along with the plaintive cry of the peacock. I can also hear fragments of conversations between the people walking down the street, waiting for a tram at the corner or meeting friends there to undertake a leisurely walk in the city through the park and up the Schlossberg[*] to enjoy the spring sunshine together. I miss the noise from the glacis just over there a little because Sunday in the city is the day of the pedestrian and the cyclist. It's a cheerful and colourful bustle out there but participation is denied me. I have incarcerated myself of my own free will because from here, from my own room, I can give in to my passion and pursue my investigations.

I'm a simple and undemanding person. Because of that my room is furnished in a very Spartan way. There is little more than the usual amenities such as a chair, a table, a bed and a wardrobe to be seen in my cellar flat. I am. therefore, a thoroughly average person and as far as the furnishing of the flat is concerned, even a little below average. The only conspicuous thing in the room in which I'm sitting at the moment as I wipe bits of clay from the table is a house altar in the corner next to my bed. Not that I believe in God, at most I believe in Goddesses. This is my corner for devotional objects I made myself from bricks consecrated to them. A brass candelabra and an altar cloth with gold thread woven into it decorate my brick construction. The candle wax falls to the floor like a petrified waterfall, lighting up a modest triptych of posters from the supermarket. Finally, completing my composition, there is a sheaf of straw flowers and a plethora of women's torsos modelled from clay, without heads, however. I purchased the

---

[*] Castle Hill

straw flowers on the farmer's market on Lendplatz, the
torsos I make myself in my leisure time, when I want
to enjoy the fruits of my researches. Incense impreg-
nates the air of my laboratory with the sweet smells
of Asia and fine veils of it float out of the window
passing on their way the armchair that is my work-
place, my observation post, my place of leisure.

HELMUT EISENDLE

(∗ 1939)

G , R , A , Z

There where home is furthest away it is most dear to
me GRAZ clock tower schlossberG lisl diet Rich-
steinplAtZ brockmannGasse RechbAuerstrasse the
sunny corner waltendorf Gymnasium federal gymnasium foR working people the apprenticeship telephone mechanics post and telegraph administration
assistant at bulme siemens & halske itt pharmaceu-
tical industry hoffmann la roche and out into the
world every thought gets lost in a falsified memory of
some spot on a map or other so why GRAZ why not
tashkent or samarkand or houston texas paris texas
or dawson city two thousand kilometres north of van-
couver where oswald wiener is sitting in the ice so
GRAZ GRAZ glimmering gRAy
                            g
genau glimmert glasharfenes glockenklingengleich
gegen ganz genaues geschichtsverständnis

*(exactly glimmering glass harp-like bell-ringing im-
mediacy set against a quite precise understanding of
history)*

r

rosenfarben rasend rasen regenbogen rückwärts rück
links ringelblumen riechend

*(pink coloured raging lawns rainbows backwards
swing left marigold smelling)*

a

aller abende ausfälle auf ausgefeilten abfallhügeln
aller aussichten aufnimmerwiedersehen

*(every evening cancellations on polished rubbish tips
all prospects goodbye forever)*

Z

zwischen zuhause zwitschern zerrissene zerwürfnisse
oder

(between home chirping inner turmoil disputes or)

GR

gurrend grAuenhaftes grauen grösster grammatiken
grollen

(cooing dreAdful dawn greatest grammatical grudge)

aZ

azul azulblau azulblauGelb azulblaugelbgRün Azul
blauGelbgRünAltrosaZitron
oder

*(azure azure blue azure blue-Green azure blue-gReen
yellow AZure bluegreen-yellowoldroselemon
or)*

GRA

graben grasbüschel grammatisch grau grallagaberl
gravaman grave gravität gravid

(digging grass tufts grammatically gray grallagaberl graveman grave gravity grapevine)

raZ

razemos razzia razzledazzle razorback razorbill razor
strob

oder

(raid, razzle-dazzle razorback razorbill razor strop or)

GRAZ

GRAZie GRAZil GRäzismus gräzist grAZe GRAZi ngshot G RAZier G RAZingland G Reen green gr AZ GRAZ all other dark and crazy cities rawly wakinG cRude opAK (opaque) sunlight and shadows in their lemon black & white streets and gassen (streets) moist pith of brea d the froggreen wormwood the matin insence court the air graZ und (and) all the other dark crazy cit ies yes the fresh Green schnapps from hArings off-licence and yes so what is graZ for me at least leadinG to a memory of my biRth my youth my schooldays my mArr iage realiZing my fatherhood my torm ent my joys till nineteenhundredandseventy- one then Gone to baRcelonA berlin munich friaul triest then vienna soon amsterdam a long zigZag way a long way home to that unknown GRAZ GReet the schlossberg for me And the older girls when i'm home at last or have no Zeal to return or once again from the beginning i do not think nostalgically about GRAZ at maurer's pub i've always eaten well then Going foR A Zestful walk Going up the Rosenberg or in stifting or the kitkAt or the bohemian or schiller court so what graZ GRAZie GRAZile dammed Gräzismus the green green grAs of graZ

GRAZ GRAZie GRAbenstrasse in the direction of
the grallagaberl pub grey history
and if that is too much it is still too little that café
europa my father playing billiards or tarock yes and
then one Glass afteR Another at Zweytick's and then
yet another and Good health gRAZzledazzle GRAZ-
zledazzle yes GRAZ indescribably lightinG up memory
very slowly An impetuous mixture GRA Z or the excuse the accomplice of literature so GRAZ it could
also have been bruck or kindberG oR pettAu or cilli
or dawson city somewhere zeroing in for the nth time.

WERNER SCHWAB

(1953–1994)

Grazart

MRS. WORM
I'm the first person above you who would welcome it
if the world would manifest a hole into which you
could lower yourself. But there isn't enough stupidity anywhere on the face of the globe that would let
someone like you into it. Just because Mr. Landlord
once bought a picture from you for his children's
room, doesn't make you a big painter with a free pass
to the world.

HERRMANN
A shameful old sow, that's what you are, wanting to
imagine me absent from the world. But the day will

come when you'll be forced to admit that the painter Herrmann Wurm first saw the light of day in Graz and that he represented it all over the face of the planet. Graz ... they'll say ... and Wurm ... they'll say ... and the inventor of the personal rays of light ... they'll say ... and small town: major art ... they'll say and quite simply Grazart ... one can predict. A real Grazart, that's not mouse shit to be eaten by a dog which then has to be run over by a lorry. And Grazart is certainly not an eaten up liver that fell out of some alcoholic corpse ... as it's being washed. And in no case is Grazart something that has no use ... *Nobody* can take Graz out of my life.

MRS. WORM
But what kind of art is it then, this Grazart?

HERRMANN
Well, Grazart ... this kind of art, that's when artistic people ... collect their sensitive feelings ... in the sensitive city ... that is, when an kind of art takes its unique beginning from the sensitive people of Graz. That's as if Mr. Landlord would say that he would need to take in a coloured picture for the children's room for children of Graz ...

But what are you saying ... always nasty questions like that escape from your nasty guts, you always strangle my voluble art for so long till it doesn't get any more air. Just as soon as my thoughts take wing like the beautiful black and white penguins, you tear the guts out of my whole art like an over-cooked boiler chicken each every black Sunday.

ALFRED KOLLERITSCH

(∗ 1931)

Memories of Wolfgang Schaukal

He suffered the end of ›Austrianness‹ and he suffered it as the end of culture. For him Austria was a »complicated complex,« standing for what culture could be despite the tendency to turn life into a graveyard or to stylise it at a most elevated and noble level. He was one of the last old Austrians, perhaps he really was the last. (Like many of *his* generation he dedicated too much of his life to Rome, to a truth he believed in and in which he finally lost himself). Immediately after the end of the war (he avoided the word collapse) he placed himself at the country's disposal.

Up on the spruce-covered mountains to the west of the almost unknown city of Graz, a city which was to become his, he experienced the end of the inopportune time politically but not mentally. He quickly realized that both politics and the life of the mind he himself had contaminated, had been left lying in the middle of the country. At a reservoir just below the village of Pack he began to combat the over-hasty hope that lay in the rubble of the future. He dedicated himself to art once again and expected that only it could show any signs of, or bring forth, something new, effect a change. He was ready to talk again for it's sake, to use his voice as a bridge into the new age. He acted on the assumption that it would come to pass, that its demands would register, especially in art, and he was prepared to be the people's educator, rescuing them on the way up out of the abyss.

In the village he met occupying English soldiers and amongst them some officers who were recuperating in villas round the reservoir lake. He was sitting in the pub with the officers as a terrible thunderstorm broke over the village, darkening the day. After a violent bolt of lightning had extinguished the lights, the land-lady came with candles. That, however, brightened it but little. He had got to know one of the officers the day before and it was with him (he spoke fluent German) that he began to speak about ›Austrianness‹ during the thunderstorm. The officer, a very well-educated Jew, was (as he remarked) surprised to find a man three thousand feet above sea level, in between the towering cliffs, spruces and firs, amongst military equipment fleeing troops had left behindwho made it possible for him to believe Austria might rise again. »You are it's physical incarnation,« said the officer, »and the brilliance of your language belongs to it as well.« In the middle of the raging storm the officer invited him to speak about Austria in that over-filled room. He did just that. Those who spoke no German were invited to follow the sound of his voice. At the end of the speech, when the sun had come out again, they were all speechless. The Jewish officer went to him and embraced him and recounted later that he had whispered in his ear that the Russians would re-treat from Semmering in a few days and that the Eng-lish High Command would take care of him.

The painter often returned to that speech as to something long lost. It had been his greatest inspiration and delusion and its effect had been felt for years, although he had effectively spoken it into empty space. It had been during the speech that he had become aware that many of the words were too heavy, weighed down with a whole century.

The people's educator who, prior to the war, had followed up the idea of educating the people in Sweden, did not like to use the word ›people.‹ He avoided the word ›heimat*‹ completely. Back then, in his speech on the mount of rubble, he had seen one thing clearly and objectively; humanity had become both rubble and God in the form of the Godless. Since painting had once been so important to him as a method of analysing perception, he loved the characteristic of the thinking Austrian to be more positivist than metaphysical. He had lived out being Austrian then, enticed by his drive towards sensuality into believing that his life then had been fulfilled, something which still tempted him even now. As a positivist, something he was despite his beliefs, he loved appearances as an investigative method and that's why he could remain silent. That's why he doubted his own images or had destroyed them immediately. The Nazis destroyed all pretences both towards the people and towards the world. Instead of that, they erected a dictatorship of the true, the good and the beautiful, the once and for all, the nothing-else-can-be-allowed-to-exist. That's

* homeland, home country.

why he suffered so long from these words and had searched so long in the world for what they meant. He was also unable to prevent himself from finding »Austrianness,« something which had never revealed itself either in the form of a lost God or as pure spirit as the spirit of the Germans had. Austrian superstructure had always been Baroque, shimmering, Catholic, shot through with tinsel but also surrounded by an abyss. It had monopolised the things of the world less, had protected them from being a comprehensible whole and allowed them to be more accessible. Thinking was less proud, less abstract, if a little colder than in other places. It was also the case that the tensions and divisions between opposites were greater and more abstruse. In this country something like a dialectic could never gain the upper hand, everything was about experience and the borders of experience. However, if you left the tensile field you reduced it on the one hand to a stupid, anti-intellectual hedonism and, on the other hand, it coagulated into a dull conservatism.

During one of the first of the night watches, (the nurse had, in the meantime, got used to it) he had her look through the old emperor's little spy window; he also told her how nice it had been for him to draw the neighbouring pane, the one with the Magna Mater Austriae, the Madonna with a sunburst halo, and to give it the correct colour. He dared to curse in front of this Madonna. »A potential Austria has passed by under your nose.« He held on to his beliefs from anger, and from where the Madonna was he had often squinted over at Rappelkopf and to the pane on which the other Austrians, the friends from his first years in the new city, were depicted. Angrily he had taken a little chisel and hammered them off, protesting with damnatio memoriae. »They have sold Austria to the new zeitgeist, a sunken modernity. They have betrayed tradition to the reactionaries.« »What would have been the right thing to do?« the night nurse asked him. »Now, as I lie dying, I can no longer tell. I leave the stove, it protects the symbols.«

After these outbursts, the night nurse had her hands full. She acted with enthusiasm. She loved the painter's face, but above all she loved his trunk. »A proud torso,« and »a deep, childlike face with sparkling eyes.« she wiped away the perspiration and allowed her arm to move up and down with the movements of his chest. She once said later, »There was a man lying there.«

In the middle of the city, the old town, working, he set up the plumb bob and watched the city carefully as he used to watch the test tubes during the first year of his chemistry studies which he had long since abandoned. He had his place, a piece of the world. He did not deny to the rest of the world that he loved the province because it was more ruthless. The belief in the wider world, generalisations, the appearance of possessing greater truth. The province frustrates this way out.

The place strengthened him to carry on looking for what he longed for. (»It has to exist,« he shouted at

314

the night nurse once.) He felt the order of the place, how it grew, the movement on the streets, buildings, squares and parks, they told him about becoming and that was more than simply planning.

From the lower reaches of the market and commercial quarter where he observed the war at work between free creativity and institutions, he recognised a rapid decline instead of improvement (in Goethe's sense) – a confusion of dilapidated buildings, miserable shops and cheap public spectacles. Day by day he went home from a house on the east side of a square (where his work was located) often accompanied by a secret friend who was like a son to him.

The path was the way to utopia, a route with often wild conversations with himself that were always despairing even then, when sunlight fell on the street and lit up the facades of the old houses. Going through a narrow alley he reached a slightly wider street, ascending, it took him past the cathedral and the mausoleum. He, who found so many things questionable, who went from one doubt to the next, from one surmounted truth to the next (he described the tile in which he had recorded Nestroy's Zerrissenen* to the night nurse), was so true to his beliefs that would not permit the church to absolve itself from the overpowering demands of its own past. He forced an eternal truth on it. He re-affirmed it every time in front of the cathedral. Passed the old university, the theatre,

---

* Someone at odds with themselves.

Freiheitsplatz[*] to Karmeliterplatz following the street that led to Glacis. He left the town centre through the old city gate, crossed the northern part of the park where his favourite tree stood, a tall elm. Where he lived had been a village once and was now a popular residential district …

The nurse sat down on his bed. She saw the painter's body relax. His beard, softened with sweat, was arranged on his cheek. His lips radiated a violet colour. His fingers, extended, were at rest and gave the impression of being smaller that when they were balled into a threatening fist. »Just like that May,« he said suddenly, »my wife and daughters dancing out of it. I made their life difficult in a nice way. Affection needs confusion, it gets added depth from it. They did what was good for me and didn't play the games of Austrian society. Tomorrow I want to see them, to look at them for a long time without talking.«

A little later, suddenly startled, he had told the night nurse to take the drawings of Penthesileia and Achilles out from under the bed. They must disappear along with him. They are the ones with most of him in them, right on his borders. She, and only she, was allowed to take them. She could give one to his secret friend and he should hide it in the darkest corner of his wine cellar.

---

[*] Freedom Square

During the three weeks she had taken care of the painter, the night nurse had travelled in a huge spiral with him, she had followed the twists and turns and listened to the contradictions. On another level (higher or lower), though, the torn and doubting man was reconciled with himself. The reconciliation was a state of desperation, the cause of destruction. She made it her duty to remember the hasty, racing speeches; the pathetic, angry, unrestrained monologues; the shouting and outrage as a continuous process of thought. He was most deeply moved that his course for Austria, which was, in 1945, a completely new beginning for him, could have been a re-awakening of the past, of history from its sleep. It would have been more appropriate if the way had only led through his head. A point of collection at the end, an identity (»a victory of stupidity«) would have been the abyss for him, even though he was often called an old ontologist. He was never able to free himself from his ideas …

URS WIDMER

(∗ 1938)

Not just the pearl of Styria

Anyhow, Graz is not just the pearl of Styria but also the city of ›the Movement.‹ At the time, we in Switzerland also saw a lot of movement but we were spared the experience of the fascists actually exercising their

dreadful power. How we achieved that is still contro-
versial, the conflict is linked with the myths that we
all carry around in our heads. In any case we made
all kinds of compromises, almost every one you can
think of and some that are almost not to be thought.
We allowed 1800 railway wagons a day full of goods
to run from Germany to Italy and the son of our most
senior General sold the Germans the barracks for
Dachau concentration camp. »In our unworthy era,«
as Friedrich Dürrenmatt said, »it is not possible to
have a thoroughly worthy position.« So we got by with
tricks and we ourselves believed that our army, our
unqualified resolve to defend ourselves and our anti-
fascism had prevented the worst from happening
while in reality it is to be feared that it was more the
fortuitous circumstances we could not influence in
any way and our lending them a hand (which was,
indeed, unworthy) that saved us. We fulfilled our
contractual duties more than conscientiously. Up to
eighty per cent of exports of our industrial products
went to the Germans during the war. Soon a neutral
Switzerland was more useful than one ›brought into
the fold‹ of the Reich would have been. In any case,
if the New Europe, which is what the Nazis called
their dream of the future, had come into being, Switzerland would have been ripe for plucking. It was to
have been a united Europe under German leadership
with a single currency, from Scandinavia to Greece,
without borders or internal customs and with standardised industrial norms and rapid communications
systems. It is a dream that is very familiar to us nowadays. A strange repetition of something that is only

similar and not the same because one thing you cannot accuse today's Germany of is being infected with racial hatred and murderous desires. Even at the time Hitler's anachronistic delusions, the core of Nazi thought, provoked abhorrence and protest both in Switzerland and in the Reich amongst industrialists and businessmen who would normally have had nothing at all against German hegemony. This wasn't because they loved the Jews or Russians so much but because you don't kill potential customers. Dead people don't buy anything. At least sections of the economy, of the Swiss economy, were more ›modern‹ than Hitler. For them, destructive wars were anachronistic instruments of the previous century. They would much rather have fought the war using economic means.

In this context, in the peace we have today which really sometimes appears to be war by other means, money has become so frenzied in my mother country, that many natives cannot afford to live in it any more. In this context, defined as it is by the economic cynicism of large concerns, population explosions and the collapse of ecological systems; the role of literature dwindles continuously. It is the role of everything which is, or appears to be, superfluous. We, here, still speak of literature. Looking at it like that, it has almost disappeared for us as well, it is as if we were looking at the book through the wrong end of binoculars. Far away. Small. Barely visible. It is up to us to stand the pressure and not to deny it. It's up to us not to give up the claim of producing some great design *and* to know how powerless we are. We must not puff ourselves up as bullfrogs do – »péter plus haut que

son cul« – as the French wisely say, without with-
drawing to out garden allotments. To walk upright
without self-pity. To learn to live with the truly dislo-
cating contradictions of our time. To come to terms
with the fact that private happiness is attainable and
that this should not only be possible if we suppress
the larger public unhappiness. By the way, a certain
amount of suppression and defence is necessary for
survival of any kind. If we felt the full force of the
death of every starving child we saw on television the
pain would kill us within a very short time.

GUNDI FEYRER

(∗ 1956)

Money corrupts

Craving to vacuum up all the dirt viz. TV: to be lazy
and lie around ›carefree.‹ Otherwise: shopping, cooking, eating in the café round the corner, Café Preinsack,
read the newspapers, eat cake. To test out the new air,
to find a place in it, to reconnoitre it, is it becoming
lighter, heavier, slowing down, what is it doing to me?
Nothing particularly appeals to me apart from a few
of the Slav sounding names on some of the shop signs
…

The city doesn't tell me anything and I don't talk to
it. I wander around, on the edge and wait for waves
to carry me out into the middle of the city or some that

wash me back up onto the beach of my existence on the edge of things.

The jaunty ring a matter of contemplating the horizon:

old worries, skirts and ironed paper are unfolded and then flattened out again: I turn my attention to my appearance often.

Then my gaze comes to rest on the waves rolling in and is pushed back to the beach into of my own eyes:

I only want to waste time and money, to live extravagantly, to throw them around me in a great arc and then to go for a walk with them ...

Nevertheless some men smile shyly at me when I catch their eye. Graz is a rich city and also, so they tell me, the most expensive in Austria.

My suspicion is confirmed – money corrupts. (Vienna is much poorer and cheaper they tell me).

But the food is better and it really is very good.

Despite the shops that enliven the city – a continuous feeling of we-would-rather-be-on-our-own.

Many women are expensively dressed (the prices for clothes are generally very high (in Paris they are very much cheaper)); they also wear a lot of make-up and my enjoyment of it conjures up a picture of the south. By leaving that picture aside, the made-up tries to blend with the unmade-up and the naked (naturalness, so-called); it is something that interests me with only a few people. (make-up: extended dress). Most of the men look stolid and boring; it can be read in their perfectly contented eyes. Powerless resignation. Up till now none of that craziness that perhaps only exists in my head; nobody who looks as if he would like to bang his head on the wall just because he feels like it. Where is this »Slavic or Hungarian« quality; am I in a border area here or not? Where are the pubs and bars I loved so much in Vienna, there were everything is topsy-turvy or those where it is so oppressively quiet that you can hear the mice running behind the wainscoting ...

ÉVA PETRÖCZI

(* 1951)

Graz, k. & k. summer

Clock tower and peacock cry
Close to resurrection requiems
Floating on a Valpolicella foam;
In the Tuscan idyll of the Styrian marches
my dashing, Kaiserjäger* grandfather Peter
winked at me
like a lovable gentle jinn
from the gossamer-fine tipsiness of the punch.

---

* An army regiment, equivalent to »The Queen's Own ...«

HERBERT ZINKL

(∗ 1929)

About Graz

I

Was it the secret writing of the reclaimed earth
of your ground plan
that forced you to the edge of history,
did the exhausted steps
on the wrong track and on the run
come to fruitful rest
at the foot of the rock at your centre –
who decides what dreams or nightmares encircle
with blooming hills
and many-coloured walls?

II

Nevertheless, never really wakened
from the dusk of your own legends
from the murky perceptions
on the banks of washed up mountains;
the rush and roar of water
like a river of words
deafens
(also those of your perennially
rebellious poets
as they pluck the petals of your
hypocritical heart
like daisies ... I love you ... I love you not ...;)
but in secret

still submissive
those eternally faithful
with the chameleon skin
who judge and absolve
even from the rejoicing
of your blood-stained balconies

III
Stay suspicious
over-hastily intoxicated pals
underhanded garden bowers
with still fermenting fruit juice
of apples, grapes and brain.
During May Days and golden autumns
the ash container
collects at whirlwind speed
the faded residue
of facile affections.

IV
Overlook the delusion of euphoric pilgrims
on shores of deceitful harmony:
in the sly country faces
under Mozart's cantilenas;
in the Tuscan facade
from Styrian granite;
in the face-lifted courtyards;
the prettified lanes
with their nasty spinsterish look;
in the baroque laughter of bells
their melancholy tolls
and peace-proclaiming thunder.

V

A friend from the south
smelled the porous, tormented mountain
in the days before the rain
looking for that fairytale
from which he once fell in reality
homesick
his undamaged sea.
This is what you, Graz
consign to him and me:
in foreign homelands to feel
incessantly the longing
to travel far
in order to come home.

MONIKA WOGROLLY

(* 1967)

The tempo is different

»I won't travel to Spain but back to the beginning in order to round off the story which is awkward and unruly,« I said to my listeners. »Where I come from everyone knows each other and gets out of you way. Or, in the lanes of the old city, they steer straight for one another. In the city it's like being in a boiler. In Vienna the wind blows. There, where I come from the air is still as if standing in a trough, further towards the south there's more air to breathe. There, there's a quagmire, a sauna, bad air, contaminated water. The way in which I approach people in Vienna, Madrid, Paris, London or Zurich differs from the way I approach people from where I come.

The pace of it is different. There, where I come from I notice many things and they get me down. Vienna frees me from that. I'm easier with myself here, I don't get caught up in things don't stand still, don't falter, flow, I'm pulled along by sounds, images and smells. You don't have to have been to where I come from. The saying is from Thomas Bernhard. But the smell of the grass in early autumn is nowhere better than there. The steadfastness of the people in the face of forlornness, a compactness of steps that are taken and sentences that are said, rustic and cosmopolitan are in love, side by side.«

»There, where I come from there are trams but no underground,« I imagined the scene further, »there, it's not like here where a Jesus-like lean youth with hollow cheeks, beard and blond hair stops you in the aisle of the underground and says, ›Excuse me but I have nowhere to stay. I'm hungry. Do you have a little money or work for me?‹ and is silently given from all sides. During which time a one-armed man is snubbed for showing his stump in public. There, where I come from, the beggars squat on the edge of the pavement and approach you directly. There, where I come from, the beggars take it personally and swear at you or run after you if you refuse them, like the poor in India. It's better, you're told, to ignore them so as not to encourage their compulsive begging.«

MAX GAD

(∗ 1954)

GRAZCOFFIN
the first day, framework for later

There lies the city in grey and dirty air, there I am, from the sloping village with a language, flotsam, grey and dirty myself, as if stamping through crusted snow with the smell of the stable, wide roofs, the stink of petrol and facade painting. And with sadistic nuns. There at last: *I'll catch my death here.*

That will be an issue.

Worn out and grey, eyes that grind, splattered with dirt. Mud on the suit, mud under the fingernails, mud on an empty face. That is the price for the journey here. Pursued by mudslides on the way, they lifted the train off the rails, they tore huge bites out of the slopes, vomited boulders into the valley. An outcry from the locomotive – wrongly interpreted, otherwise we would have gone back and be somewhere else now. Some place or other (later it will be called Lungau) we're told – get out of the carriage immediately and run. We run along slopes, suddenly a cemetery comes at us, steep and fast and resolute. Wreathes, snaky ribbons, flowerpots, rubbish and rubbish and a bench and more rubbish. Wooden crosses shoot down the slope like torpedoes straight at your shinbones. We wade and stagger, arms stretched out wide, confused Christophers in clay water, slipping and sliding through silt, over all a strange and sublime silence. I know I'll be waiting for something better for a long time. In a coupe abandoned in flight lies a ludicrous hat, corduroy, bought by grandmother. On arrival it's noticeable the hat's missing. *Where is the hat?* Forgotten. *Forgotten?* The lie becomes an issue.

And: what is important in a catastrophe.

At the goal at last and without a hat. In the railway station a poster from the Esperanto aficionados. Comforting. A Pez[*] vending machine. Nothing can happen to you here. The first legend mumbled prematurely in the train concerned the Maiden's Leap: *from the top of the cliff to her death at the bottom.* Whether the maiden jumped or was pushed, that was something the narrator disputed with herself. Then the houses, they have narrow shoulders, squatting pointedly and bitterly like left-over aunts, and that's just how it smells here as well. In the village there was air and space in spite of the rocky cliffs into which the railway line is chiselled. There in the village which planted depravity the war was only on the periphery. That dawned on us as a supposition, later. Here the people cannot stand the looks, shake their heads before you're finished with the question, they consist of a sullen subservience, their signals: *don't talk to me. Not in Esperanto either.* They give no or false information. I'm eleven and think: when the suit is brushed

---

[*] A small oblong hard-sugar sweet.

they'll be different. Theme: From the pathetic principle of hopefulness. Roundabout everything is hurried, urges and rushes. Less towards a goal and more like away from something. This question will stay: from what? My question will be: where to?

My question stands.

By tram down into the greyness of the people and streets. Into the depression. Into squashed breath. Conductors bark, dogs whine, people are in the middle of the real thing. I am looking (theme:) for the remembered pictures. I saw them time and again, earlier, turning the pages of »Mein Österreich, mein Heimat*,« Vienna 1914. Later I would put both folios on the scales (why, really?) – I've forgotten the occasion – 6.4 kilos. Included in this weight are the Ruthenian farmers. Costumes from Bukovina. The astronomical clock in Prague. Figures from Kaiser Maximillian's grave in the Hofkirche near Innsbruck. Bagpipe players from Galicia. Fiakers** from Vienna. South Tyrolean peaks and the Tatras. Crakow's Municipal Theatre and the house where I was born, theme. That it is to be found in the same book as Budweis and Budapest and as Trieste and Sarajevo and means I feel infinitely familiar. Don't the Kopaničari from Mähren look like American Indians? Ah, romanticism, it's your own fault. Now I'm looking for the bell tower, bell chimes, university, Anastasius Grün. I can't see

---

* My Austria, My Homeland
** Horse-drawn coaches

any of it, the city has been exchanged, the old palaces imitated in cheap materials. The other one has completely (theme:) disappeared. A crowd of nothing but imitations, nothing real as it is in the sepia photographs. Too exhausted to be surprised.

Theme: Wonder, Exhaustion and the Opposite

Looking for the uncle who was supposed to pick us up. Theme will be: A man of his word. His father and my grandfather (to whom the folios belong) got on with each other. Instead of following our instincts in the streets, we follow the next best pointing finger and become the blind leading the blind, runners off at tangents, running gags. The next ignored sign, grandmother. And onwards. Uncle's wife starts, a canary in a dark kitchen, looks beaten but nevertheless very unmarried. No gesture to take a seat, no clothes brush. Theme: hospitality and the weight of being polite. In a voice that retraces itself all the time she stammers where he can be found, perhaps. Then the first escalator of my life. And onwards. The impression that lacks expression: everything is stage scenery here and in the midst of it you play urban dweller, awkwardly and with exaggeration. Later (later comes often and remains a theme) I paste invisible memorial plaques, my own legends: thirty years from now a deserter from the south will walk with me along the streets continuously greeting people left and right and say: *this is home*. Sentiment is something for the Front and that is something you don't understand. On that first day I wasn't ready for it. And onwards. You can't tell from looking at him that I'll buy a xylophone from that the second-hand dealer sometime, a present for my child, for whom I am both St. Christopher and the donkey and that is still to be born. It still has to be conceived. For that (theme:) she has to be found. The she it will be about and already is. *Here I grab onto life.*

Theme has been and will remain: Illusion. And (typing error) nwards.

He roars, wears a signet ring, continuously touches his blow wave and works for the building inspectorate. He found us a house as specialist and relative. Midday in a stinking pub near the park (it'll be called the Fröbel) he makes fun of the rustic burr in my speech. Dagmar's harsh speech, blond above the laugh that I'll never kiss and Kurt's as well. He is my pew neighbour and always has to kneel in front of the priest. This latter, fat as a cliché, doesn't want to get up for the beating. *Can't you help me?* – What? – *Shit on the crucifixed swine in the confessional – a matter of honour.*

Goodbye, Lending lustre to the one left behind.

The found uncle encircles the room with a homely gesture: *I'm a Nazi, and in there, there are only Nazis.* They look like quite normal people. That will be the theme, what else could it be. He moans he needs a convertible. Grandmother lays a pile of money, a brick in grease-proof paper, on the pub table. And another journey, this time in a bus. Petrol stations and decrepit factories. Buildings where it isn't clear: are they are being built or torn down? At the terminus, a long march, passed a ruined castle, the shattered, stinging-nettle windows, passed murky shops, rejected people with distrustful gazes, desperate slyness . Hoarse dogs who throw themselves against the fence in a frenzy of tearing around and still they don't tear it down. Uphill again, steep again.

No cemetery flooding towards me, but a future nevertheless. First of all passed this bloated, old, grey, more and more dirt overflowing the enamel chamberpot in the courtyard. Brings up whore's children, the girls beautiful, just like their mother. Sometime later grandmother will give her a marble slab for safekeeping. *For the grave stone.* When she dies and the marble is needed,the old woman won't know anything about it anymore and will threaten with the toilet brush.

It's shit here – more than elsewhere? – eternal theme. Like: Fraud Like: Money. Like: Errors. Like: Beauty.

Viewing: The house for the brick has been built from narrowness time height of the concrete stairs, from the rottenness of the window frames, the lowness of the rooms, deep cracks in the walls. On the ceiling brown water colour as if it had been thrown up there by a moor. *For so little*, said the expert, *the optimum.* Grandmother, let's go back. Her face so pale. *Or do you know anything better around here?* From the upper terrace I look at the Schlossberg in the distance, see the dialectic of this city: it lures you from far away.

Once you're here, the only thing you want to do is to leave. Until it's far enough away to lure you in order to reject. Grandmother signs and believes unwaveringly that this scoundrel will be tormented by a bad conscience. The money had gone to the devil. Uncle is on good terms with the previous owner, they go off to celebrate. *Delightful to have idiots as customers, a gift of the gods.* Later I'll say: Why should he treat us any differently to all the others? Soon – naivety has long been a theme, also with the hand-me-down paltriness of my symbolism – the oath: *I'll shit on your grave you Nazi swine of a relative.* An oath is holy. But before we get that far, his wife, the gloomy canary, falls from her perch. At the funeral I scratch the convertibles face. At the moment my occupation is not to look grandmother in the eye. A bad (theme:) witness of her (theme:) bitterness und (theme:) shame.

That's how the city begins for me, and it's becoming chronic.

February 2002

ALFRED KOLLERITSCH

(∗ 1931)

No: Graz: Yes

Who says? What is the city? How is will formed? The number of offices a city has reflects the needs; administers human needs and activities, satisfying them.

Communal life needs organisation. If someone thinks he *is* in the city without being influenced by it, he doesn't understand it properly. Virtue and vice »are defined« in the community, the city is a conquered and unconquerable world at the same time, the world is the openness of the encounter, a petrified form of the public. Now, whether one is of the opinion that the public is a product of false political and economic manipulation or that it wants to be ruled without the rules themselves having to be justified by reasons (this form of the concept »there has to be order« has met with the least resistance in Graz up till now) both opinions *fail* to deal with the complex processes of change, especially the altered demands made on the legitimation of power. The ideals of right and left, as revealed in these two opinions, have to confront the possibility that a new intellectual culture is opening up, one which has not yet been assimilated and which attempts to make plans for managing the future. It would be fatal if the established powers could simply make the new culture disappear into the old channels. The observation that neo-conservatism acts more swiftly is a signal. In the mourning of the Left, the desire for new ideas (free-thinking) once again withered under the denunciation that it was simply a new edition of false consciousness.

New ideas wither all too easily when they are dealt with simply as an alternative, in the confusion of private myths behind which the short-circuited yearning for order often stands, a dive into redeeming nature.

I think that Graz, indeed the whole of Austria has had the chance to have an intellectual culture like this, but that no-one was able or willing to grasp it *other* than from a party political standpoint. As happens so often, it was pushed into the corner labelled ›art and intellectualism‹ and countered with ›practical necessity,‹ avoiding intellectual luxury and cleaving to system-strengthening traditions. The suspicion that the practical necessities could take on an entirely different aspect if one approached the world other than from a purely economic position; that it needed a new spirit; was not considered, although lack of spirit is just as bad as lack of work.

Tolerated out on the margins, the city allows itself a few spring shoots, it communicates little of that to its citizenry. It looks for attractions for the tourist industry and had no truck with those who felt foreign in their own city and whose foreignness annulled any possible culture for Graz. Until genealogy reports on them. Reciprocated love displaces shame. Shame that befalls so many of those who think about their heimat[*] today, who can no longer think the word *heimat*.[*] Reciprocated love is like the dog that once came into the kitchen.[**]

No: Graz: Yes.

---

[*] Home country, town, district.
[**] Reference to a folk ditty: A dog came into the kitchen and stole and egg from the cook; the cook cut the dog in half; along came a pack of dogs and dug a grave for the dog. On the gravestone they wrote: A dog came into the kitchen …

JOHANNES KOREN

(∗ 1939)

Came, stayed and often returned

Many Viennese say, »Graz is a provincial nest.« Some Grazers say it as well and, having taken a group tour to New York, China, Melbourne or Grado,[*] they want to show with this sentence what globetrotters they are.

H.C. Artmann never said it and these lines are being written on the day he died.

He always felt at ease in Graz with his poet friends and the painters with whom he like to drink calmus at Haring's so much. He never talked very much when he was there, but when he did say something it was always a piece of that poetry which was so much a part of him and which he recited in such an incomparable way. To read his poems and prose was, and is, a pleasure. To be there when one of his works of word art became a completely original work of art in his mouth, was a gift.

It was through this poet of the world as much as anything else – the way he strolled through Stadtpark to read from his works in Forum Stadtpark and to be together with those of like mind, to be silent with them or to talk to them – that it became evident that the term »nest« could also mean sheltered and cared for in a place where you are able to think, write poetry, analyse and renew yourself.

---

[*] A small Italian seaside town very popular with Austrians as a summer holiday destination.

H.C. must have felt here in Graz what poets, painters, sculptors, composers, musicians, photographers,
singers, actors and media artists of his age and much
earlier had also felt. There has got to be a reason why
they came here and stayed, or at least always came
back even though better chances were on offer elsewhere. It was like that even at the time of someone
like Anastasius Grün, Robert Hamerling and Peter
Rosegger; at the time of the architect Hauberrisser;
the painters Zoff, Scheu, Damianos and Thöny and
the musicians Wilhelm Kienzel, Robert Stolz and
Karl Böhm. In their era Graz was an intellectual centre and a cultural backdrop with doors and windows
open for the fresh air of the innovation, just as it was
almost fifty years ago with the new awakening with
the Styrian Autumn, the Forum Stadtpark. Even today Graz is a nest, in the best sense of the term, for
all those who consider life to be more than just about
satisfying basic needs. How, in particular, that can be
felt I found out in the last year of the 20th century
during a pre-Christmas stroll through the city. There
I encountered many of the great names of our time
from the world of art. I met them in bookshops and
cafés, but also in quite ordinary places, often camou-
flaged with a plastic bag from LIBRO or BILLA.[*]
Gerhard Roth came out of a bookshop and could have
used a pack horse. Only a few steps further on the
father-poet of Graz, Alfred Kolleritsch, came along
but a little slower, not quite as hectic as he used to be,

---

[*] The former is a chain of office supplies, music and book shops,
the latter a supermarket chain.

and only a few metres away the poet Klaus Hoffer appeared giving support to his wife during the Christmas shopping. Herwig von Kreutzbruck with his walking stick hurried down along Sporgasse, a ruddy face talking sotto voce about his dead colleagues Gunter Falk, Klaus Schöner and Werner Schwab who were always to be seen around here. Immediately behind him Otto Kolleritsch the rector of the Music University appears, head lowered, drawn into the city to meet an important music person. The author Günter Eichberger darted round the corner like a weasel probably on the look out for a theme for his column in one of the Graz papers. On top of that Andrea Wolfmayr came striding along. The vagaries of life caused her to change from the world of poets to that of politicians and she was perhaps asking herself what, other than a regular income, attracted her to it. In Lueggs, on one side of the main square, Markus Schirmer, the great pianist, was chatting to the actor Wolfram Berger, perhaps about the next project after their evening »Angels in your Head.« Everyone who saw that evening has fond memories of it. Hair flowing, stage star Gerhard Balluch rushed out of Sackstrasse while the multi-talented artist Joachim Baur was on his way to his »workshop« and half way up Sporgasse just crossed Günter Brus' path, almost colliding with Gerti Pall and Otto David because of the effusive exchange of greetings. They had apparently just come from the Schauspielhaus. In Herrengasse every second person was an artist, journalist or cultural manager and it was amusing to look on and see how friendly they all were to each other.

George Traversa was there and so was the architect Wallmüller, the painter Fritz Panzer and jet another architect, namely, Klaus Kada. Retired provincial governor Dr. Krainer came round the corner out of the Hans Sachs Gasse not getting very far because of his »bath in the crowd« and already involved in a conversation with Günter Waldorf, the doyen of the Graz painters and who was, in turn, rummaging around in his bag of ideas.

A Christmas market had been built up on Tummelplatz. The architect couple Szyszkowitz-Kowalski, the best advertisement for the Graz School, rooted around in the things on offer and looked over to the Academic Gymnasium in which the painter Hartmut Urban who died much too prematurely had taught. You would certainly have been able to find him here, in this bustle of artists. In Bischofsplatz, where it was getting a little quieter, a group of poets stood, Wolfgang Bauer at the centre telling stories. Not even a hundred metres further on was a convocation of painters, right next to the door to the »Gallery Atelier.« Mata Wagnest, Gustav Troger and Michael Kienzer stood there deep in conversation. The gallery owners Benedikt Steinböck and Eugen Lendl came from the Mausoleum down through Abraham-a-Sancta-Clara-Gasse, in a state of unusual harmony and almost bumped into Emil Breisach, one of untiring motors in the cultural life of Graz, in Glockenspielplatz. They looked over to what used to be Harings with melancholy. It was a spirits and liqueur pub where – as we know – H. C. Artmann, Gerhard Rühm. Michael Scharang, Helmut

Eisendle, Ernst Jandl and, of course, Wolfi Bauer and Alfred Kolleritsch drank a lot of bitter calmus and were able to re-invented the world. As my steps were taking me through this colourful swirl, Alois Hergouth, the doyen of contemporary Styrian poetry, lay out in Maria Grün, chained to his bed in Anton-Wildgans-Way just as he had been before, in his »cave« in Moserhofgasse. Surrounded by pictures, presents from his artist friends and lovingly cared for by Gerda Klimek and Sepp Trummer who organised a very special Christmas tree for him every year, one on which each friend could send his greetings from the world outside into the sick-room, a visible sign of having a little time for him. Hergouth now journeys between the world of his memories and an uncertain future and looks back on the »creative brew of Graz« which he, along with others, stirred with such vigour. Not even those whose gaze is fixated as if by remote control on the year 2003 can change that.

After this stroll through the past and present I wonder if we would not be well advised to think about the present and to support the young, ambitious artists of today with their exceptionally lively creative potential. Without the city's artists all the art houses wherever they are, whether or not they will be completed on time, would have been built in vain and the title of »Cultural Capital of Europe« would remain empty words.

MONIKA MERTL

(* 1955)

A Surprising Avowal

Right from the beginning Harnoncourt's home city of Graz has proved itself the setting for special events. It was there in 1985 that the festival »styriarte« was founded as a platform for the »famous son« of the city and his work which pointed the way ahead. It was a surprising avowal of a living artist, a political initiative a few moments before an economic recession and intended to counterpoint the »Steirischen Herbst.« The annual series of concerts in Graz which are about to be augmented by opera productions thus reflecting Harnoncourt's own voyage of discovery from early baroque to the edges of the twentieth century. Many sensational performances such as Schubert's spiritual drama »Lazarus« or Schumann's oratorio »Das Paradies und die Peri« have taken place exclusively for the »styriarte.« The record company was not always prepared to share part of the risk the organisers had assumed.

But anyone who might think that Harnoncourt rules the Graz Festival as Karajan once did in Salzburg, is over-estimating his propensity to interfere when others know what they're doing. The »styriarte« enables him to realise many projects close to his heart, independent of the »mainstream« and the dictatorship of marketing. That happens on the basis of common interest. In the fifteen years of his project a workable, future-oriented and comprehensive concept has ripened. It perceives Harnoncourt's idea as being an impulse and develops it further independently without requiring every programme decision and artist contract to be submitted for approval.

It was during the »styriarte« 1987 that Harnoncourt first met the Chamber Orchestra of Europe. Haydn's London Symphonies provided the promising prelude. Thereafter the co-operation shifted to the area of the German romantics which for Harnoncourt meant the early nineteenth century above all – Schubert, Beethoven, Mendelssohn, Schumann and finally Brahms. They are tailor-made enterprises in which the interest of the conductor and that of the orchestra go hand in hand. Together with the Chamber Orchestra he developed a romantic sound which makes the existential depths and a feeling for the absurdity of life in this oft down-played epoch perceptible, without betraying its longing for beauty and harmony. The audacious spectrum of the Romantics' expression, often premature in fruition and ending in premature death, is unmistakeably echoed in the youthful mentality of the musicians.

He develops, most notably in the context of Schumann, a modern idiom free of cloying sweetness. For fully six years Harnoncourt and the Chamber Orchestra were engaged during the »styriarte« with Schumann's symphonic and musical drama works. The authority that devolves on the individual tonal vocabulary of this fascinating »Zerrissene[*]« can be seen from a number of live recordings. A number of important new interpretive approaches are successful, especially in the violin concerto and the opera »Genoveva«.

Has »Don Quixote,« who once set out from the German Romantics, arrived at his goal? It appears that a circle has been completed, but there are signs that indicate something much more. The first contact with Wagner's »Tristan« is already on the programme. This step will also be taken together with the Chamber Orchestra of Europe. Even now a similarly structured young ensemble specialising in the interpretation of contemporary music has put

out feelers seeking cooperation. Who knows to what adventures he can be tempted in the dawning twenty-first century.

GÜNTER EICHBERGER

(* 1959)

A funny Styrian with a Slovenian accent

I often notice that I don't really see Graz any more because I'm so used to everything here, houses as much as people. Only one thing can help then, to talk about the city with foreigners. People like the curator Vanesa who comes from Slovenia and is studying art history in Graz.

---

[*] *a person at odds with themselves.*

What did she notice first? That the natives spoke German. But not the German she had had to learn in a course but rather a strange variation of it which remained incomprehensible to her for a long time. In the meantime she speaks a funny Styrian with a Slovenian accent. It might be a cliché: in the beginning she could not stop being amazed at the diversity of goods on offer in our department stores. In her birthplace, a village near to Maribor, you cannot buy avocados, amongst other things. Instead there was a lot of corruption in Slovenia. And no serious newspapers.

Incidentally, she likes Vienna less than Graz. (This has to do with the inhabitants). She quickly made the acquaintance of the Grazer late-bohemian scene. Between »Trattoria« and »Mild« she became involved in a web of relationships having to do with conspiratorial art circles. In this milieu alcohol flows in rivers and for some there is a threat of drowning. Luckily she is not conscious of being addicted.

FRIDO HÜTTER

(∗ 1950)

Good Morning, Graz!

»You don't have to have been to Graz.« This subordinate clause from Thomas Bernhard's »Heldenplatz«[*] is so right that it sounds almost wrong. Let's put it like this – one should have been to Graz. There is almost no other place where you could have observed such a strange development. Graz catapulted itself out of the role of a sorrowful old hag into a cultural children's paradigm, waiting there with unrelenting patience for years before showing recent tentative signs of a developing adolescence.

The starting point for this strange route lies half a century in the past. At the time the people of Graz greeted their ›VerFührer‹[**] so happily that he gave it the fatal title »The City of the People's Uprising,« which resulted, after a rude awakening in 1945, in the people lying down again, with a vengence. Pensionopolis they called it.

You can only leave Graz. Not something Bernhard said but he would have been right with that as well. Robert Stolz, Karl Böhm, Otto Loewy and many oth-

---

[*] Historical square in the centre of Vienna. Literal translation: Heroes Square.
[**] Verführer + Führer = Seducer + Leader

ers went. Some went of their own free will, others were expelled and never invited to return. Peter Handke sharpened his pencil here and went. Arnold Schwarzenegger inflated his first muscles here and went. Many others followed. Only a few came back. Dead, like Grand Prix World Champion Jochen Rindt.

Then it was Forum[*] and then it was Herbst.[**] In 1968 as young Europe was manning the barricades, as cars burned in Paris and free love was practiced in Commune 1 on the communal mattress in Berlin, Graz also woke up. In its own way, that is. Old barricades were cleared away but the only thing that burned was the zeal for the new; wild sex took place mainly in the theatre. Authors such as Gerhard Roth, Harald Sommer and, above all, magician[***] Wolfgang Bauer wrote scores for the sudden, violent spring in Graz which took place in the »Steirischen Herbst.« Adelhard Roidinger, Eje Thelin, John Preininger, Dieter Glawischnig delivered the soundtrack. Dieter Pochlatko, Curt Faudon the film of the story. Emil Breisach and Alfred Kolleritsch acted as chief ideologues.

The political authorities tolerated it. To be quite honest they orchestrated part of it – pars pro toto Hanns Koren, provincial councillor from the Austrian Peo-

---

[*] Forum = Forum Stadtpark = arts festival)
[**] Herbst, literally autumn/ Steirischen Herbst = annual arts festival)
[***] Wolfgang Bauer wrote a play called »Magic Afternoon«)

ple's Party* who inspired and encouraged the »Jungen Wilden« such that the political explosive power of the cultural revolution was re-directed into the safer territory of art. From that time on, as a sort of side effect, the conservatives of the Steirmark have kept the sceptre of applied avant-garde in their own hands.

All of a sudden there was more coming to Graz than going from it. People like Eugene Ionesco, Laurie Anderson, Bob Wilson, Bill Fontana, Günter Brus, Christof Schlingensief and many others felt comfortable in the city in which you were allowed to do absolutely anything- Graz – city of the People's Revival.

Heroes are also susceptible to being awarded tenure. And it can't always be »autumn.« And so Graz went from being an oscillating avant-garde laboratory to become a kind of artistic letterbox company. One could relax in the comfortable knowledge that nice regular excitement would be delivered right to the door; that Graz's good reputation had spread out from Ljubljana to Lübeck and that the German arts section in the newspapers would increase that every »autumn.« The little love child slowly started get used to being an infant that lived from the sweet milk with the good brand name. Spoilt by all the lethargic joys of the province.

It's just ten years ago now that the city of culture began to show signs of saying farewell to the senile kinder-

---

* Conservative Party

garten. There were fights about an art centre and fights about a civic hall – and both were built. Forum Stadtpark was allowed to go through a cathartic phase of quasi-extermination only to be resurrected. The museum flagship Joanneum was brought back onto something verging on a recognisable course. Schlossberg was rediscovered. Vito Acconci was permitted to place his island in the Mur whose water were not nearly so murky as the once were.

Art was being brought out of the galleries and museums. It was re-animated by ontologically first-class performances. It was manifest in design colleges and intelligent industry. It popped up as magnificent Popculture at SK Sturm.[*] It sneaked into almost everyone's consciousness in great style.

It's often said that the avant-garde is always shot in the back. Yet another rule that doesn't apply to Graz. A home-made fake suicide apparently turns out to be a healing and stimulating nap. – Good Morning Graz!

----

[*] SK Sturm = Sporting Club Sturm = football team

WOLFGANG LORENZ

(∗ 1947)

Graz – who would have thought it?

Well, who would have thought it, that within such a short period of time Graz would get three noble titles from the civilized world – European Capital of Culture, put on the World Heritage List and City of Human Rights. Pretty heavy, What happened? Just this: in the mood around the change of millennium the city fathers (and mothers) took a look at their sleepy child and decided – it can't go on like this. European matura[*] or something, at last.

Childhood years after the war more or less spent, more or less hard at work, cleaning away brown stains and re-building. But rather depressed. Then suddenly the full onslaught of puberty, especially in autumn. Cultural revolution. Chairman Koren, an intellectual light sword, adored the adolescents instead of spanking them. And was at first spanked for it and then adored.

International Avant-Garde moved into the city. Nothing was certain anymore. Styrian autumn storms heated up the young, the old shivered. Cold – hot, as is normal in puberty. The Forum Stadtpark was Graz' successful kitchen which didn't want to serve folk

---

[*] Final school examination at the age of around 18 which functions as university entrance qualification.

dishes. International whispers, gossip, boos. The children took over the up-bring of the city and their provincial fathers (at that time there were almost no mothers). Exasperating sexual offensiveness, generational conflict and so on. Big grins and dread despair all over the place. (The Austria 68ers only noticed in the 70s that the 80s shouldn't be like the 50s). Not a few Grazer whistled continuously in the cultural woods, letting off steam and giving themselves courage; they shook on princely thrones and had less fear of Vienna. Processual works and working everywhere, actions and reactions alternated with each other merrily. Sounds good, was good and then at some point it wasn't so good anymore because it really wasn't anything but a memory anymore. The Styrian autumn wind rustled down through a decade and through changing, waggly dentures, was becalmed and produced, at best, a yes, mmm, right.

Then final peace, silence, deathly silence that was to be heard everywhere. Devotions in front of Koren icons, post-korenic corrosion, so to say. A return to traditional values instead of progress. In between the Graz School of Architecture opened, thank God. New start, international attention. A new intellectual »gründerzeit« with massive results. Many good houses in and around Graz. Then, political collapse. The possibility of courageous house building as a form of cultural therapy was gambled away.

A mood mixture of resignation and depression became the negative stimulation of the cultural Grazer. Misery everywhere – the best thing is to get out of here! Only the notoriously bad train and flight connections held a handful of creative people in Graz. They felt as if they were in Duckburg; the new Uncle Scrooges were stingy with any form of contribution. It was too little to live on and just a little too much to die from. Or something like that, that was how the situation was depicted to transient travellers who were asked to pass on final words of greetings to the world. But it wasn't like that really, but how real is the reality of he who is the suffering subject? But here is the objective report. The mood of the late Eighties and early Nineties was miserable, cultural ups and downs.

At some point it must have been enough for everyone and so, in the middle of the Nineties a fresh wind began to blow. The remaining Grazer and newcomers by accident of birth began to squirm and stretch in their self-imposed full-body corset and so this seam or that seemed to burst by itself. Curious heads popped up, one limb or another signalised a spirit of enterprise, arms reached out, legs stepped up. Anyway, animation like this produced enough insight, which became certainty, that if things continued as they were, especially accepting the conspiratorial theory that the whole world was against Graz, then it would kill off the lust for life. A civilised biotope which had continuously felt itself neglected began to feed itself substantial amounts of oxygen.

The ways of the world round about did the rest. The Grazer understood more and more that Graz was a place that offered them everything they needed to live anyway, perhaps even survival rations for the battle for its place in the world. A new self-confidence, and new sense of self-esteem arose. People started to understand that most of what happened in Graz (or didn't happen) was the same as elsewhere. Graz was not so unique, except for being uniquely beautiful, of course. Compliments to television, it offered a taste of world salad in its satellite dishes. All of this led, at some point, to the completely unexpected but powerful shove that Graz gave itself. The depressive gaze left the ground and fixed itself on the horizon and just look, it found itself in the middle of Europe again. And Europe was looking back at it. The eye contact with the world had been re-established.

Right in the middle of this dawn of a new era, it was possible to convince the Viennese Federal Government to be *for* Graz, at least in Brussels. And that's what happened in 1998 when there was a fight there for the title of European Capital of Culture for 2003. Great Grazer, great Viennese. And then it was one thing after another. Placed on the World Heritage List, European City of Human Rights, environmental city and car cluster. On top of that, the re-building of the synagogue, the erection of a long overdue City Hall, the daring cathedral in the mountain with its campanile of lifts, the extension of the legendary Forum Stadtpark, the founding of a House of Literature, the fine prospect of a children's museum, a House for Youth Culture, new railway station, new main square, new street lighting and yes, that, the most important sign of a new change of heart – the end of a two decades-old wasteful fight for a Kunsthaus, a house of art. White smoke over Graz, under no circumstances to be mistaken for smog.

Graz – who would have thought it? All that has happened in the last few years – Graz has accepted itself again, is curious about itself, considers it has a future in a Europe of the future. This is not a contribution to the continuous Grazer election campaign but an factual description from one who is in love with Graz.

The nomination for the title of the European Capital of Culture really did effect a change. The temperature of the city's body shot up in a flash and with the self-generated feverish excitement about the magic year of 2003, all viruses, germs and bacteria of the past were killed off. Everybody is an expert about the future nowadays, everyone wants to be in the bull's eye of the target market. Naturally there are problems with the disciplines' obligatory and voluntary exercises but its no longer a case that only the prognostications are right. Positive minorities have become capable of becoming majorities.

The actual cultural capital programme doesn't really have to happen anymore. The main effort has already happened; heads re-think, the heart of the city beats strongly, a stiff breeze of anticipation and fear of embarrassment blows through Graz. Those given to euphoria locate Graz north of Semmering[*]. Up till now Styrian Autumn was only a cultural season. Recently there is a Styrian spring too. If one grasps the opportunity it will be easier to stand summer and winter – in Graz. Who would have thought it?

---

[*] Vienna, Semmering and Graz lie on a north/south axis.

»It has something southern about it,« he said, »almost like Padua,« someone remarks about Graz in Friederike Mayröcker's story »In Winter.« With that, the essence of the city is addressed with sensitivity and in point of fact this city was once the capital of Inner Austria, an region covering the Alps to the Adriatic. It was here that various peoples, languages and cultural forms encountered each other and they made the appearance of this city unmistakable. This can be read really well in the palaces and houses of nobles and citizens. The plans for these and many public buildings were also drawn up by architects from Venice and Friaul or from the Slovenian region.

In its geo-political position, the city always considered itself as a bridge to other cultural areas, especially to south-east Europe. Thus students from Timisfoara, Zagreb, Pecs, Trieste, Ljubljana or Sarajevo have completed their studies at universities in Graz. Ivo Andric from Bosnia, who later went on to win the Nobel Prize for Literature, may be mentioned here as representative of many others. He wrote his thesis in Graz in 1923-4, completing his studies with a doctorate.

Due to its geo-political position Graz has had a very chequered, if not tragic, history. Through the centuries the city was a bastion of Christianity against the crescent moon even though the Ottomans appeared only twice before the city and never laid siege to it. The city way the inhuman bastion of Catholicism against Protestantism; Lutheran books were burned in 1600 and Johannes Kepler, like many others, had to leave the city because of their beliefs. In the 19th and especially in the 20th centuries, the bastion policy led to a »defensive« posture against the Slavic southeast under National Socialism; to a catastrophe. In 1938 Graz was awarded the dubious title »City of the People's Uprising,« but the blaze in the Jewish Temple during the »Reichskristallnacht« had already announced the coming inferno.

The inhabitants of the city had forgotten their centuries old history which had been characterised by encounters with people of various nationalities and different cultures. The southern, the Mediterranean, that made the city so open and warm was lost, the political cold of northern climates seeped in. In »The Capuchin Crypt« Joseph Roth deals with this aspect and prophetically makes the point: »the dentists ... from Linz, Graz, and Knittelfeld, the goitred creatures from the Alpine valleys, they all sing ›Die Wacht am Rhein‹. Austria will perish at the hands of the Nibelungen fantasy ... Austria's essence is not to be central, but peripheral ...«

After 1945 the inhabitants begin to deal with the difficulties of re-building. In the area of culture the city was paralysed for a long time because of having been cut off for too long from new ideas abroad in Europe. However at the end of the 50s a new spirit was stirring in the generally static intellectual landscape. Young artists break the city's intellectual petrification with a »revolution,« the Forum Stadtpark is founded. Graz becomes, with the help of the important literary periodical, »manuskripte,« one of the main centres for literature in Europe. Music too, along with photography and architecture which would lead to the »Graz School«, won for themselves new importance. All of this together led to the avant-garde festival the »Styrian Autumn.« In this context, Hanns Koren's »triangular« notion reminds one of the once large, open cultural area of the city.

With the opening up of Europe, Graz is facing new possibilities and is in the process of using them. As the »City of Peace,« »City of Human Rights,« as a city of the »World Cultural Heritage« and as »European Cultural Capital.«

The editors' task of putting together an anthology of texts about Graz for the series EUROPA ERLESEN which is especially important in times such as these, initially appeared to be an easy one to achieve. The basic idea always remained the same – to approach the essence of the city primarily through literature although, in the cultural context of the city, there were some ›non-literary‹ names which could not be omitted. However, as time went by the mountain of manuscripts grew and grew, name after name appeared and in the end, sadly, it was only possible to make a limited selection. Due to this abundance and the tradition to do without chapter titles in this series it is nevertheless necessary to draw attention to the fact that the editors did intend to emphasise certain focal areas in their selection. So the first colourful chapter not oriented on history is called *Graz Impressions* (p. 27–71) the those thereafter are ordered chronologically in the interests of easier reading: *travelling to Graz* (p. 71–96), *historical Graz* (p. 99–146), *letters to and from Graz* (p. 146–165), *cultural events* (p. 167–232), *places in Graz* (p. 237–269), *Graz in literary works* (p. 272–327) and *Graz today* (p. 333–349) This compilation makes one conscious of the intellectual wealth of the city. In the sphere of literature Graz was and is an important metropolis of the German-speaking region.

Many people have thought about this book, many have helped to collect the gems it contains. Ms. Johanna Flitsch from the Museum of the City of Graz should be thanked for her proof reading. Thanks also to Gerhard Melzer and Gerhard Fuchs of the Franz Nabl Institute for their advice. Herbert Piwonka and Hans Lambauer also deserve thanks. They did exemplary work in the inexhaustible sources of the Province of Styria Library with great success for this book.

In the play »Heldenplatz«[*] Thomas Bernhard has one of his characters, Frau Zittel, say in passing: »Graz is not somewhere you have to have been.« You, dear reader, may nevertheless feel like going to Graz in order to savour it.

Markus Jaroschka
Gerhard Dienes

---

[*] Heroes Square, a major square in Vienna.

Ivo Andrić (1892–1975). *Pupils and students from Wische-grad/Wischegrader Schüler und Studenten.* From: Die Brücke über die Drina, Eine Wischegrader Chronik. Aus dem Serbischen von Ernst E. Jonas. (c) 1992 Carl Hanser Verlag, München-Wien, pp. 326–327.

Anonymus, *Here the General took up quarters/Hier hat der General seine Wohnung genommen.* (Napoleon in Graz, 1797). From: Franzosen in Grätz im Jahre 1791, 1. Booklet, Graz 1859.

H. C. Artmann (1921–2000), *graz.* In: H. C. Artmann gedichte von der wollust des dichtens in worte gefasst. Residenz Verlag: Salzburg, Vienna 1989, 5. 22; (c) 1989 Residenz Verlag, Salzburg und Vienna. *News from North and South/Nachrichten aus Nord und Süd.* In: H. C. Artmann, Nachrichten aus Nord und Süd, Residenz Verlag: Salzburg, Vienna 1978, pp. 61–64. (c) Residenz Verlag, Salzburg und Vienna.

Anatol E. Baconsky (1925–1977), *Mehlplatz.* From: Anatol E. Baconsky, Wie ein zweites Vaterland. Verlag Styria, Graz-Vienna-Küln, 1978, p. 86.

Felix Mendelssohn Bartholdy (1809–1847), *Yawn/Zum Gähnen.* From: Wolfgang Suppan, Felix Mendelssohn Bartholdy in Graz. In: Blätter für Heimatkunde der Steiermark 36, 1962, p. 78.

Rudolf Hans Bartsch (1873–1952), *The province throws open its windows/Das Land reißt die Fenster auf.* From: Rudolf Hans Bartsch, Zwölf aus der Steiermark, Staakmann Verlag, Leipzig 1908, p. 54.

Wolfgang Bauer (b. 1941), *Graz.* From: Graz von innen, Grazer Autoren über die Stadt. (c) Literaturverlag Droschl 1985, S. 41; *In the middle of driving snow/Mitten im Schnee-*

treiben. From: Wolfgang Bauer, Ionesco und die Urania (Wolfgang Bauer zum 60. Geburtstag Ionescos, in der Münchner Abendzeitung vom 25. November 1972.), *That was »Haring's«/Das war die »Haring«*. In: Zukunft beginnt im Kopf, Festschrift 75 Jahre Urania, Published by Markus Jaroschka Caesar Walter Ernst, (c) Leykam Verlag, Graz, 1995, p. 203–204.

Stephan Benditsch (um 1800), *The Poor of the City/Über die Stadtarmen.* In: Topographische Kunde von der Hauptstadt Grätz, Graz 1808.

Ludwig Biró (1898–1972), *The Jewish community in Graz, 1938/Über die jüdische Gemeinde in Graz,1 1938.* From: Ludwig Biró, Die erste Hälfte meines Lebens. Erinnerungen eines Grazer jüdischen Rechtsanwalts von 1900–1940. Pub by Christian Fleck, (c) Literatur-Verlag Droschl Graz, 1998, p. 221ff.

Hugo Blotius (1534–1608), *Schlossberg/Der Schloßberg.* In: Österreichische Nationalbibliothek, Wien, Codex 8944.

Karlheinz Böhm (b. 1928), *In my father's city/In meiner Vaterstadt.* From: Mein Weg. Erinnerungen. Scherz Verlag Bern-München, 1991, p. 71–77. (c) Presseagentur Lionel von dem Knesebeck, München

Ludwig Boltzmann (1844–1906), *Letter to Hermann von Helmholtz in Berlin, 1872/Brief an Hermann von Helmholtz in Berlin.* From: Ludwig Boltzmann, Leben und Briefe. Pub. Walter Höflechner, Publication From: the Archive of the University of Graz, vol. 30, Akademische Druck-und Verlagsanstalt Graz-Austria, 1994, pp. 1113–1115.

Otto Breicha (b. 1932), *Wilhelm Thöny, painter/Der Maler Wilhelm Thöny.* From: Otto Breicha. Wilhelm Thöny. Sein Werk im Rupertinum. Verlag Galerie Welz, Salzburg, 1997, p. 29. (c) the author.

Emil Breisach (b. 1923), *There are ghosts going around/
Die Gespenster geh'n um.* From: Wider den Strich. Pub.
Heinz Hartwig, (c) Leykam Verlag, Graz, 1993, p. 39–41.

Wolf Dieter Brinkmann (1940–1975), *The Image of the
Night Sweeper/Das Bild des nächtlichen Straßenkehrers.*
From: Rolf Dieter Brinkmann, Rom, Blicke, das neue buch
rowohlt, (c) Rowohlt Taschenbuch Verlag, Reinbek bei
Hamburg, 1992, p. 144–145.

Max Brod (1884–1968), *Graz is like Zürich/Ähnlich Zürich.*
From: Max Brod, Reise Lugano-Mailand-Paris. In: Max
Brod/Franz Kafka, Eine Freundschaft. Reiseaufzeichnungen.
(c) S. Fischer Verlag GmbH, Frankfurt am Main 1987.
Aufgenommen in Franz Kafka, Reisetagebücher. Fischer
Taschenbuch Verlag, Frankfurt am Main 1994

Aquilinus Julius Caesar (1720–1792), *Mur suburb/Murvor-
stadt.* From: kaiserl. ko(e)nigl. Hauptstadt Gra(e)tz und
aller daselbst befindlichen Merkwu(e)rdigkeiten nach der
berliner und potsdammer Beschreibung eingerichtet. Durch
Aquilinus Julius Ca(e)sar. Erster Theil, Salzburg 178,
167ff.

Elias Canetti (1905–1994), *It embarrasses me/Es macht
mich verlegen.* Rede zur Verleihung des Nabl-Preises der
Stadt Graz im Jahre1975. From: Uber Franz Nabl. Aufsätze,
Essays, Reden. Pub.. Von Kurt Bartsch, Gerhard Melzer,
Johann Strutz. Verlag Styria, Graz Vienna Köln, 1980, pp.
177–179.

Mechthild Curtius (b. 1939), *The Cerrini palace on Friday
morning, 4th May 2001, 4 a.m./Das Cerrini-Schlössel am
Freitag morgen, 4. Mai 2001, 4 Uhr.* From: Mechthild
Curtius, *Grazer Geschichten.* (c) the author.

Ingeborg Day (b. 1940), *Where are the Jews/Wo sind die
Juden.* In: Ingeborg Day, Geisterwalzer. Residenz Verlag:
Salzburg und Vienna, 1983, p 21. (c) Residenz Verlag,
Salzburg und Vienna.

Ernst Decsey (1870–1941), *Schubert.* From: Von Schuberts Beziehungen zu Graz. In: Festschrift zum 6. Deutschen Sängerbundfest in Graz, 1902, p.16–20, *Salome.* From: Ernst Decsey, Musik war sein Leben. Lebenserinnerungen. Deutsch-Verlag, Vienna-Stuttgart-Basel 1962, p. 71ff.

Hans von Dettelbach (1900–1976), *Peter Rosegger, Wilhelm Kienzel and »Salome«/Peter Rosegger, Wilhelm Kienzl und die »Salome«.* From: Steirische Begegnungen. Ein Buch des Gedenkens. Graz 1966, p. 245. (c) the heirs

Gerhard M. Dienes (b. 1953), *The Name/Der Namen.* (collected by the author), *Against the Turks/Gegen die Türken.* From: Gerhard M. Dienes, West-östliche Gedanken. Über das Verhältnis zwischen Orient und Okzident. In: 2001 und eine Nacht. Teppiche und Textilien aus Privatsammlungen, Katalog Stadtmuseum Graz, Graz 2001, p.15. *The Old Town in Danger/Die Altstadt in Gefahr.* From: Gerhard M. Dienes, Ziegelgeschichten. In: Graz Dach. Ziegelgeschichten. Zwischen Ton, Kupfer und Gold. Wieser Verlag, Klagenfurt/Celovec 2000. p. 40ff.

Günter Eichberger (b. 1959), *The Symbol/Das Wahrzeichen. The City of the Black Rainbow/Die Stadt des schwarzen Regenbogens.* From: Graz. Stadt des schwarzen Regenbogens. Graz von innen, Grazer Autoren über die Stadt. (c) Literaturverlag Droschl, Graz 1985, pp. 108–113; *A funny Styrian with a Slovenian accent/Ein lustiges Steirisch mit slowenischem Akzent.* From: Ehemalige Feinde. Erstdruck »Stadtflaneur«, Kleine Zeitung, 12. 3. 2000. (c) the author.

Helmut Eisendle (b. 1939), *G , R , A , Z.* In: Graz von innen, Grazer Autoren über ihre Stadt. (c) Literaturverlag Droschl, Graz 1985. pp. 38–40.

Gunter Falk (1942–1983), *The way to the lucky star/Der Weg zum Glucksstern.* From: Literaturzeitsehrift Sterz, 15/Winter 1980, p. 22. (c) unknown

Gundi Feyrer (b. 1956), *Money corrupts/Geld verdirbt.*
From: Gundi Feyrer, Auswendige Tage. Grazer Tagebuch.
(c) Literaturverlag Droschl 1997, pp. 10–19.

Ernst Fischer (1899–1972), *Homecoming/Heimkehr.* From:
Ernst Fischer, Erinnerungen und Reflexionen. (c) Rowohlt
Verlag, Reinbek bei Hamburg, 1969, pp. 90–96.

Helmut W. Flügel (b. 1924), *Nobel Prize Winners/Nobel-
preisträger.* From: Alfred Wegeners vertraulicher Bericht
über die Grönlandexpedition 1929, Graz, Publications
From: the archive of the University of Graz, Graz 1990, (c)
Universitäts-Verlag

Sigmund Freud (1856–1939), *A postcard to Martha Freud
from Graz, 1904/Eine Postkarte aus Graz an Martha Freud,
1904.* From: Sigmund Freud, Unser Herz zeigt nach dem
Süden. Reisebriefe 1895–1923. Ed. by Christfried Tögel
unter Mitarbeit von Michael Molnar, Aufbau Verlag, Berlin, 2002, p.178.

Erich Fried (1921–1988), *The Stairways of Graz/Die Treppen
von Graz.* From: Einbruch der Wirklichkeit. (c) Verlag
Klaus Wagenbach, Berlin 1991, NA 1995. s. a. Erich Fried,
Collected Works, Verlag Klaus Wagenbach, Berlin 1993

Barbara Frischmuth (b. 1941), *Graz: Key City/Graz – Schlüssel-
stadt.* In: Graz von innen, Grazer Autoren über ihre Stadt.
(c) Literatur-Verlag Droschl 1985, pp. 42–44.

Max Gad (b. 1954), *GRAZCOFFIN/GRAZSARG. The first
day/Der erste tag. framework for later/gerüst für später.*
From: LICHTUNGEN – Zeitschrift für Literatur und Zeitkritik,
Graz, Nr. 90/2002, pp. 4–6. (c) the author.

Galileo Galilei (1564–1642), *Letter to Johannes Kepler in
Graz/Brief an Johannes Kepler in Graz.* From: Johannes
Kepler, Dokumente zu Lebenszeit und Lebenswerk, Ed. by
Walther Gerlach/Martha List, Ehrenwirth Verlag München,
pp. 70–73.

Anatol Ginelli (b. 1927), *The gothic double spiral staircase/ Gotische Doppelwendeltreppe*. From: Anatol Ginelli, Verdoppelnde Überschneidungen. Die Grazer Zwillingswendeltreppe. In: Daidolos, Bertelsmann, Gütersloh, Nr. 22/1986, pp. 54–55.

Peter Glaser (b. 1957), *Arrival in Graz/Ankommen in Graz*. From: Graz von innen. Grazer Autoren über ihre Stadt. (c) Literatur-Verlag Droschl, Graz 1985, p. 92.

Mathias Grilj (b. 1954), *Schizoid but relaxed/Schizophren, aber locker*. (c) the author.

Franz Grillparzer (1791–1872), *On the Way to Italy/Auf der Reise nach Italien*. From: Vol. 16, Reisetagebücher, 1. Tagebuch auf der Reise nach Italien (1819), Grillparzer's complete works. p. 124–125. *For a Friendship Book/In ein Stammbuch*. From: Grillparzers complete works. Complete edition in 16 volumes. Vol. II, Gedichte II, Ed. Moritz Becker, Max Hesses Verlag, Leipzig, p. 101.

Eugen Gross (b. 1933), *Josef Plečnik on his way to worldwide fame/Josef Plečnik auf dem Weg zur Weltgeltung*. (c) the author.

Reinhard P. Gruber (b. 1947), *Graz is splendid/Graz ist herrlich. The sausage stand/Der Würstelstand*. From: Graz von innen. Grazer Autoren über ihre Stadt, (c) Literaturverlag Droschl, Graz 1985, pp. 61–64.

Hélène Haluschka (1892–1974), *Secret Magic/Geheimer Zauber*. Unpublished manuscript From: the author's estate, 1957.

Joseph Freiherr von Hammer-Purgstall (1774–1856), *Magic Cauldron/Zauberkessel*. From: Ode an die Steiermark. In: An der Schwelle zum Orient. Intro. & selected by Dr. Ludwig Weber, Das österreichische Wort, Stiasny-Bücherei, Vol. 13, Stiasny Verlag, Graz und Vienna, p.23.

Peter Handke (b. 1942), *I was strangely proud of him/Ich wurde eigenartig stolz auf ihn*. From: Peter Handke, Das

Ende des Flanierens. (c) Suhrkamp Verlag Frankfurt 1980, pp. 20–21, *The tried and true meeting places are also the right ones for learning/Die bewährten Orte der Sammlung seien auch die richtigen für das Lernen.* From: Peter Handke, Versuch über die Jukebox, (e) Suhrkamp Verlag, Frankfurt 1990, pp. 86– 88.

Nikolaus Harnoncourt (b. 1929), *Wartime/Kriegszeit.* From: Monika Mertel, Vom Denken des Herzens. Alice und Nikolaus Harnoncourt. Eine Biographie, (c) Residenz Verlag, Salzburg und Vienna 1999, pp. 36–38.

Ingram Hartinger (b. 1949), *Summer in Graz/Sommer in Graz.* From: Literatur und Kleinformat. Österreichische Gegenwartsautoren in der Neuen Kronen Zeitung 1972–1981; Ed. Gerhard Fuchs; (c) Residenz Verlag Salzburg, 2002, pp. 90–92.

Jaroslav Hašek (1883–1923), *The Captain and his Orderly/ Der Hauptmann und sein Putzfleck.* From: Jaroslav Hašek, Die Abenteuer des braven Soldaten Schwejk. Intro. by Alfred Polgar, Büchergilde Gutenberg, Frankfurt am Main 1958, p. 110.

Raoul Hausmann (1886–1971), *A Letter/Ein Brief* From: manuskripte. Zeitschrift für Literatur 1960–1995, Forum Stadtpark Graz 1995, o. S. (c) Marthe Prévot.

Friedrich Hebbel (1813–1863), *Lodged at The Wild Man/ Stiegen im Wilden Mann ab.* From: Friedrich Hebbel, Tagebücher 1843–1847, vol. 2, Deutscher Taschenbuch Verlag, München 1984, pp. 336–342.

Alois Hergouth (1925–2002), *A Cheerful Park/Heiterer Park.* From: ÜBERGRAZ, Eds. Brigitte und Gerhard Balluch, Verlag für Sammler, Graz 1993, pp. 64–65, *The Garden at the Edge of the Gravel Pit/Der Garten vor der Schottergrube.* From: Alois Hergouth, Der Mond im Apfelgarten. Manumedia Schnider Verlag Graz 2001, pp. 68–75. (c) Georg Frena.

Fritz von Herzmanovsky-Orlando (1877–1954), *Masked Ball/Maskenspiel*. From: Fritz von Herzmanovsky-Orlando, Das Maskenspiel der Genien. (c) Residenz Verlag, Salzburg, 1989. p. 175ff.

David Herzog (1869–1946), *The Burning of the Temple in Graz on Reichskristallnacht/Der Brand des Tempels in der Reichskristallnacht in Graz.* From: Erinnerungen eines Rabbiners 1932–1940. Publication From: the archives of the University of Graz, Vol. 32, From: a thesis by Andreas Schweiger, ed. Walter Höflechner, (c) Akademische Druck-u. Verlagsanstalt Graz-Austria 1995, pp. 47–48.

Klaus Hoffer (b. 1942), *Amongst the stinging nettles in the rubbish/Zwischen Brennesseln der Unrat.* From: Graz von innen. Grazer Autoren über ihre Stadt, (c) Literaturverlag Droschl, Graz 1985, pp. 53–54.

Karl von Holtei (1798–1880), *Liebenau.* From: Karl von Holtei, Vagabunden. Roman. Breslau 1887, p. 171.

Bernhard Hüttenegger (b. 1948), *The so-called Mountain/Der sogenannte Berg.* From: Zwischenlandschaft. In: 850 Jahre Graz. 1228–1978. Festschrift, ed. Wilhelm Steinböck, Styria Verlag, Graz Vienna Köln, 1978, p. 440.

Frido Hütter (b. 1950), *Good morning, Graz!* (c) the author.

Ernst Jandl (1925–2000), *»manuskripte«.* In: manuskripte – Zeitschrift für Literatur, 1960–1995, ed. Alfred Kolleritsch/Franz Weinzettl, Forum Stadtpark Graz, 1995

Markus Jaroschka (b. 1942), *home/heimat.* In: die unruhe in den sätzen. J. G. Bläschke Verlag, 1983, p. 71. (c) the author.

Erzherzog Johann von Osterreich (1782–1859), *The Magistrate does not have the best of reputations/Der Magistrat hat nicht den besten Ruf.* From: Josef Riegler, Die Notlage der steirischen Bevölkerung zu Beginn des Jahres 1817.

Ursachen und Lösungsmöglichkeiten aus der Sicht Erzherzog Johanns. In: Mitteilungen des Steiermärkischen Landesarchivs, vol. 32, Graz, 1982, p. 74.

Gert F. Jonke (b. 1946), *That Time Before Getting to Graz/Damals vor Graz*. From: Damals vor Graz. In: manuskripte – Zeitschrift für Literatur, Kunst und Kritik, Nr. 29/30/1970, p. 92.

Dževad Karahasan (b. 1953), *The Identity of the City/Die Identität der Stadt*. From: Wer ins Schwarze trifft, hat alles andere verfehlt. From: translated From: the Bosnian by Barbara Sax. In: Ich bin ich, weil du du bist. Hrsg. Verein ISOP, Graz, pp. 37–40.

Marie Luise Kaschnitz (1901–1974), *I stood there and listened/Da stand ich und hörte zu*. From: Marie Luise Kaschnitz, Tage, Tage, Jahre. (c) Insel Verlag Frankfurt 1992, pp. 106–107 & 110–111.

Paul Anton Keller (1907–1976), *Rag Market I/Fetzenmarkt I*. From: Paul Anton Keller, Jahre, die gleich Wolken wandern. Erzählungen aus einer Kindheit, Anton Pustet Verlag, Graz-Salzburg-Wien, 1948, p. 267ff.

Johannes Kepler (1571–1630), *Letter to Galileo Galilei in Parma/Brief an Galileo Galilei nach Parma*. From: Johannes Kepler. Dokumente zu Lebzeiten und Lebenswerk. ed. Walther Gerlach/Martha List, Ehrenwirth Verlag München, p. 73.

Wilhelm Kienzl (1857–1941), *The Austrian Premiere of Salome in Graz, 1906/Die österreichische Erstaufführung der »Salome« in Graz 1906*. From: Dr. Wilhelm Kienzl, Besprechung der Oper »Salome«, Freitag, 18. Mai 1906, Grazer Tagblatt, vol. 16, Nr. 135. (c) Dr. Johanna Broda

Joseph Carl Kindermann (1744–1801), *The French occupy the city/Die Franzosen rücken ein*. From: Joseph Carl Kindermann, Repertorium der Steyermärkischen Geschichte.

Geographie, Topographie, Statistik und Naturhistorie, Verlag Franz Xav. Miller, Grätz 1798, pp. 219–220.

Hans Kloepfer (1867–1944), *City of the Volkserhebung/ Stadt der Volkserhebung.* In: Das ist Graz. Die Stadt im deutschen Südosten. Intro. by Hans Kloepfer, Graz: Steirische Verlagsanstalt 1938, p. 10. Quoted in: Christian Ehetreiber, Die Touristische Mobilmachung der heimlichen Literaturhauptstadt, in: Stadtkultur-Kulturstadt. Eine Bestandsaufnahme aus Anlass des Europäischen Kulturmonats, Graz, Mai 1993, pub. by Gerhard Melzer, Graz, 1994, p. 278ff.

Alfred Kolleritsch (b. 1931), *Reciprocated Love/Gegenliebe. We are who er are/Wir sind wir. If you could ward off the love of this city, you would leave it/Könnte man sich der Liebe zu dieser Stadt erwehren, würde man sie nie verlassen. Castle Rock Tunnel II/Schloßbergstollen II. No; Graz; Yes/ Nein: Graz: Ja.* Excerpts From: Gegenliebe. In: Graz von innen, Grazer Autoren über ihre Stadt. (c) Literaturverlag Droschl, Graz, 1985, p. 21–34, *Memories of Wolfgang Schaukal/ Erinnerungen an Wolfgang Schaukal.* From: Der letzte Osterreicher, Roman, (c) Residenz Verlag, Salzburg Vienna, 1995, pp. 17–22, 88–89.

Hanns Koren (1906–1985), *That's how it was meant to be from the beginning/So war es gedacht vom Anfang an. Looking for A New Way in New World/Einen neuen Weg in eine neue Welt zu suchen.* From: Eröffnungsrede zum »steirischen herbst 1968«, In: 10 Jahre steirischer herbst, Ed. Paul Kaufmann, Mundus, Österreichische Verlagsgesellschaft, Vienna 1977, p. 8–9.

Johannes Koren (b. 1939), *Came, stayed and often returned/Hergekommen, geblieben, immer wieder gekommen.* From: Stadt der Künstler. In: Johannes Koren, Skizze von Graz, Satiren, Pamphlete, Phantasien, Betrachtungen. (c) Verlag Steirische Verlagsgesellschaft, Graz 2001, p. 25–30.

Walter Koschatzky (b. 1921), *The never particularly conformist capital/Die niemals sonderlich konformistische Hauptstadt*. From: Wilhelm Thöny, 1888–1949, Exhibition catalogue, Graz/Triest n.d., (c) unknown. *A Picture by Paul Klee/Das Bild von Paul Klee*. From: Walter Koschatzky, Faszination Kunst. Erinnerungen eines Kunsthistorikers, (c) Böhlau Verlag, Vienna, 2001, p. 80.

Karl Kraus (1874–1936), *Captain Prasch/Hauptmann Prasch*. From: Karl Kraus, Die letzten Tage der Menschheit. Bühnenfassung des Autors, ed. Eckhart Früh, With drawings by Georg Eisler and an essay by Eric Hobsbawm, Suhrkamp Verlag, Frankfurt am Main-Wien, 1994, p. 303ff.

Angela Krauß (b. 1950), *Graz*. (c) the author.

Joseph Kyselak (1799–1831), *A Beautiful Chestnut Allée/ Eine schöne Kastanienallee*. From: Zu Fuß durch Österreich. Skizzen einer Wanderung selbst einer romantisch pittoresken Darstellung mehrer Gebirgsgegenden und Eisglätsscher unternommen im Jahre 1825 von Joseph Kyselak, nachgegangen und nachgedacht von Ernst Gehmacher, Verlag Fritz Molden, Vienna München Zürich New York, 1982, p.28–29.

Heinrich Laube (1806–1884), *Fried Chicken and Pints/ Backhendln und Seidln*. From: Hans Lohberger, Johann Gottfried Seume in Graz. In: Blätter für Heimatkunde der Steiermark. pub. by Historischen Verein für Steiermark, vol. 47, Graz, 1973, pp. 89–92.

Dora Lauffer (1907–2000), *Protestant Bride. Catholic Groom/Protestantische Braut, katholischer Bräutigam*. From: Dora Lauffer, Die Wellen. Alt-österreichische Familiensaga zwischen Adria und Schlesien. Re-constructed by Maria Lauffer-Ossiach and family documents, Graz 1989, p. 209 (c) Akademische Druck- und Verlagsanstalt

Hans Leifhelm (1891–1947), *The essence/Vom Wesen*. Leykam Verlag 1958, 4. Auflage, p. 10. (c) the heirs.

Kenka Lekovich (b. 1963), *That time in St. Petersburg/Damals in Sankt Petersburg*. Deutsche von Primus-Heinz Kucher. (c) the author.

Wolfgang Lorenz (b. 1944), *Graz, who would have thought it?/Graz, Wer hätte das gedacht?* From: Programmbuch 2, Graz 2003, Kulturhauptstadt Europas, Medieninhaber: Graz 2003, Kulturhauptstadt 2003, pp. 5. 3–9. (c) the author.

Karel Hynek Mácha (1810–1836) *Let's wait for the horrendous bill/Harren wir der horrenden Rechnung*. From: Karel Hynek Mácha, Die Liebe ging mit mir … Prosa, Poesie, Tagebücher. DVA, Tschechische Bibliothek, 2000, pp. 354–356.

Claudio Magris (b. 1939), *Liebenau Penal Barracks/Strafbaracke Liebenau*. From: Café San Marco. In: Claudio Magris, Die Welt en gros und en dètail. (c) Carl Hanser Verlag, München Wien, 1999, 21ff.

Alma Mahler-Werfel (1879–1964), *Gustav Mahler at the premiere of Salome/Gustav Mahler bei der Erstaufführung der Salome*. From: Alma Mahler, Gustav Mahler Erinnerungen. (c) Fischer Taschenbuch Verlag GmbH, Frankfurt am Main 1991

Thomas Mann (1875–1955), *What a talented skittle-club friend/Was für ein begabter Kegelbruder*. From: Thomas Mann, Doktor Faustus, Band VI, Complete works in 12 vols. S. Fischer Verlag GmbH, Frankfurt am Main 1960, pp. 204–208. (c) Bermann-Fischer Verlag, Stockholm 1947

Friederike Mayröcker (b. 1924), *In the Winters/In den Wintern*. From: Friederike Mayröcker, Gesammelte Prosa. (c) Suhrkamp Verlag, Frankfurt am Main 2001

Max Mell (1882–1971), *The Bad Mistress/Die schlimme Meisterin*. From: Max Mell, Steirischer Lobgesang, (c) Insel-Verlag, Leipzig 1993, pp. 104–108.